METHUEN'S MONOGRAPHS

ON PHYSICAL SUBJECTS

General Editors: B.L.WORSNOP, B.Sc.,Ph.D.
G.K.T. CONN, M.A.,Ph.D.

Particle Acceleration

Particle Acceleration

J. Rosenblatt

Université de Paris
Faculté des Sciences–Orsay

METHUEN & CO LTD
11 NEW FETTER LANE · LONDON EC4

First published in 1968
© 1968 *J. Rosenblatt*
Printed in The Netherlands by
Nederlandse Boekdruk Industrie N.V.

Distribution in the U.S.A.
by Barnes & Noble, Inc.

Preface

Early particle accelerators were almost exclusively used for research in nuclear physics. Furthermore, nuclear physicists were often designers and builders of their own machines. Builders and users, anyway, did not find it difficult to understand each other. The situation now has drastically changed. Many new 'customers'–biologists, chemists, physicians, solid-state and high-energy physicists–depend on accelerators for their research. Machine building has become the province of groups of specialists whose connections with the problems faced by the users are perforce rather loose. Naturally, most of the numerous review articles, papers, books and symposia on the subject reflect the experience of people engaged in the design and construction of accelerators. This monograph is meant as an exception to the rule. It is intended primarily for those who are concerned with machines mainly as research instruments, but must nevertheless learn the principles of their operation. The basic concepts of course remain the same whatever the point of view, but the above consideration has dictated the choice of material. Emphasis has been put on questions such as possibilities and limitations of different machines or their beam structure in space and time rather than on magnet design, ion source operation or detailed descriptions of individual accelerators. The interested reader will find thorough treatments of these subjects in the literature quoted at the end of the book.

The different types of accelerators have been treated in a manner which is neither elementary nor fully specialized. Calculus has been freely used throughout, but all mathematical calculations are preceded by qualitative discussions. The tables and numerical examples included are meant to convey that order-of-magnitude feeling which forms an essential part of the knowledge of any physical subject. I hope that this approach will make the book useful not only to those who have to make use of accelerators but also to undergraduate students taking a course on these machines.

For the purpose of this edition, the material in my previous book

(*Aceleradores de Partículas*, Lautaro, Buenos Aires, 1960) has been completely re-worked. Many subjects required an altogether different treatment and certain new machines, such as tandem Van de Graaff generators, had to be described. The outcome has been a new book, which I expect is more in accordance with the standpoint I mentioned above.

The first two chapters are of an introductory nature. The first is a necessarily brief sketch of the many contributions of accelerator research to our knowledge of matter. The second is a reminder of the fundamental laws of mechanics, electrodynamics and relativity essential for the understanding of accelerator operation. The different types of accelerators are described in Chapters 3 to 7, while the last chapter is devoted to future possibilities.

As will appear from the text, many laboratories and individuals have contributed with photographs, graphs and information to the making of this book. I am happy to thank them all.

My thanks also go to the Argentine Consejo Nacional de Investigaciones Científicas y Técnicas (Scientific and Technical Research Council) for their support during the writing of this book.

I should like to express my gratitude to my wife for her permanent encouragement and for undertaking the tedious task of typewriting the manuscript.

At different stages the manuscript was read by Mr. W. Schimmerling and Professor J. A. Evans. I am indebted to them not only for their comments on the subject matter but also for their help in eliminating the foreign traces still present in my written English.

Buenos Aires, June 1966   J. ROSENBLATT

Contents

CHAPTER 1

Particle Accelerators as Research Instruments

Towards the end of the nineteenth century, when the investigation of atoms and molecules was just beginning, the scientist's position was compared with that of a man locked in a room, on the walls of which there are wheels, levers, pulleys, all sorts of mechanical devices. A concealed mechanism operates behind the walls, producing unexpected movements among the paraphernalia whenever a lever is touched. The man cannot but press different levers and analyse the resulting motions to understand the nature of the hidden mechanism.

The same picture applies to the present state of our knowledge of atomic nuclei and elementary particles. Although mankind has been able to make practical use of nuclear forces their full understanding is still lacking. This is not due to the scarcity of experimental facts; on the contrary, what is missing is a coherent explanation of all or at least the majority of them. Although important steps in this direction have been taken in recent years, unifying different and apparently contradictory models of the nucleus, much remains to be done. In the meantime, there is no other choice but, in accordance with the above picture, to carry on acting on the hidden mechanism through the available levers. The subject matter of this book is in fact one of the most important 'levers' of nuclear physics: particle accelerators. Their purpose is to produce beams of electrically charged particles of very high speed, from about 10 000 km/s to 300 000 km/s depending on the type of accelerator. The latter figure is the velocity of light and, according to the theory of relativity, the maximum possible speed that a material particle can attain.

The particles most often used for acceleration are electrons and nuclei of light elements, such as protons, deuterons and alpha particles. Lately, heavier nuclei, such as those of carbon, beryllium, oxygen and neon, have also been accelerated. The most important characteristics of these particles are given in Table 1.1.

Accelerated particles are mainly used in the manner shown in Fig. 1.1.

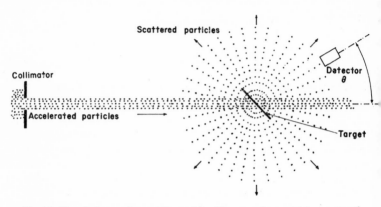

Fig. 1.1. Use of a beam of energetic particles. The secondary particles leaving the target in different directions are counted by detectors, which may also sort them out according to their energy, charge or mass.

TABLE 1.1
Particles most often used in Accelerators

Name	Symbol	Charge	Mass	Composition
Electron	e, e^-	-1	1	elementary
Proton	p, H^1	$+1$	1836	elementary
Negative hydrogen ion	H^-	-1	1838	1 proton + 2 electrons
Deuteron	d, H^2	$+1$	3660	1 proton + 1 neutron
Triton	t, H^3	$+1$	5500	1 proton + 2 neutrons
Helium 3	He^3	$+2$	5500	2 protons + 1 neutron
Alpha particle	α, He^4	$+2$	7290	2 protons + 2 neutrons
Carbon nucleus	C^{12}	$+6$	21857	6 protons + 6 neutrons
Oxygen nucleus	O^{16}	$+8$	29150	8 protons + 8 neutrons

Charge and mass are given in terms of the electronic values, $1·602 \times 10^{-19}$ coulomb and $9·108 \times 10^{-28}$ g, respectively.

The particles form a beam which is directed against a piece of matter called the target, thin enough so that the particles may traverse it without appreciable energy loss. As a result of their interaction with the atomic nuclei in the target some particles are deflected away from their initial paths, or may knock out particles of a different type. The nuclei in the target are separated by distances of about 10^5 times their own diameter*. The target therefore has the appearance of a widely spaced lattice, through which most of the incident particles pass without collisions. The scientists generally investigate the interactions due to the few particles that come close enough to the nuclei in the target. The resulting effects depend on the type and energy of the incident particles; electrons, for example, having a negative charge, are attracted by the nuclei and repelled by the atomic electrons in the target. They lose energy by collisions both with atomic electrons and nuclei, and this energy appears in space in the form of electromagnetic radiation from the target. Collisions with atomic electrons generally result in low-energy x-rays (up to a few hundred keV†) while, provided that the incident electrons are sufficiently energetic, collisions with nuclei may induce the emission of radiation of a few MeV, known as γ-rays. We have thus met one of the first applications of electron accelerators; the penetrating x-rays obtained from them have been and are still being used for the treatment of cancer.

The interaction with nuclei becomes more important as the energy increases. Electrons will be scattered in all directions, and their angular distribution may be studied by means of detectors, as shown in Fig. 1.1. At energies above 200 MeV this is a powerful method for obtaining information about the nuclear radius and the distribution of protons within the nucleus. At even higher energies (above 600 MeV) electrons can probe not only the structure of nuclei but that of isolated protons and neutrons as well. It has been shown, for instance, that neutrons are not strictly uncharged, but have an internal distribution of positive and negative charges which averages out to zero.

The situation changes radically when the beam is formed by particles

* The nuclear radii go from $1\cdot5 \times 10^{-13}$ cm for hydrogen to $9\cdot3 \times 10^{-13}$ cm for the heaviest elements, such as uranium, whereas atomic radii are of the order of 10^{-8} cm.

† The electron volt (abbreviated eV) is the energy gained by an electron when traversing a potential difference of one volt. One keV = 1 000 eV; 1 MeV = 10^6 eV. See Chapter 2 for further details.

other than electrons (protons, deuterons, etc.). These are atomic nuclei and therefore positively charged, which implies that they will be electrically repelled by the nuclei in the target. The collisions with atomic electrons result in a gradual energy loss as the particle traverses the target. A second and more fundamental difference arises from the fact that the forces between nucleons are not only of electromagnetic character. This conclusion follows from the very existence of atomic nuclei; in fact, if only electric forces were present the protons would repel each other and no stable nucleus could exist, with the possible exception of hydrogen. Therefore a different type of force, generally called the nuclear force, must be responsible for holding the nucleons together. When atomic nuclei are used as projectiles, this force will influence their scattering, thereby providing information about its nature.

The fundamental nature of nuclear forces has not been fully explained. Certain facts have however been established; one knows, for example, that they are of very short range (of the order of 10^{-13} cm). Furthermore they must be quite strong, since the electrostatic repulsion between two protons at such a distance is of about 23 kg (10^{28} times their own weight). Because of these forces 'nuclear matter' is so compact that its density is $3 \cdot 5 \times 10^5$ tons/mm^3. We therefore have two forces acting between incident particle and target nuclei, the electrostatic repulsion, effective at large distances, and very intense nuclear forces which become dominant when the particles are extremely close together. It is evident that nuclear forces will mainly act on those incident particles which have sufficient energy to overcome the electrostatic barrier created by the target. In Fig. 1.2 the magnitude of the electric barrier for incident protons is plotted as a function of the atomic number Z of the target. In this figure the maximum energies which can be attained by different types of accelerators are also shown. The single-stage electrostatic Van de Graaff generator, with a maximum energy of 8 MeV, can therefore be used to produce nuclear interactions in targets with atomic number less than 28, whilst a cyclotron of 20 MeV has practically no limitations. Thus, each machine has a well defined range of applicability. Low-energy accelerators, for example, are suitable for high precision studies of light nuclei. In recent years experiments on what is known as Coulomb excitation have been carried out. These are based on the very small probability that a particle of low energy has of traversing the repulsive barrier of heavy nuclei. In fact, even though the particle may not reach the nucleus, it can get sufficiently close to yield part of its energy through the electric field. The nucleus then makes a transition into what is known as an excited state and finally loses its excess energy by emitting a γ-ray. By measuring the energy of these rays and the distribution of scattered particles, information about the internal motion of the nucleus and its shape can be obtained.

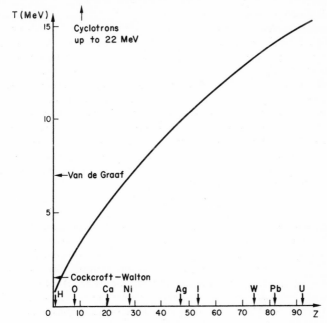

Fig. 1.2. Electrostatic barrier encountered by protons impinging on target nuclei of atomic number Z. Particles having two, three, etc. elementary charges suffer a correspondingly greater repulsion.

Accelerators of intermediate energies (linear accelerators, cyclotrons) are particularly useful for the study of nuclear reactions. These include the following processes:

(*a*) The incident particle hits the nucleus, then leaves in a different direction from its initial one. If there is no change in the state or composition of the nucleus, this process is called elastic collision.

(*b*) Due to the collision, the nucleus makes a transition into an excited state, from which it returns into the original one by emitting a γ-ray. The incident particle is deflected and loses kinetic energy. This is called an inelastic collision.

(*c*) The nucleus captures the incident particle and then emits a different one or a γ-ray. These are the nuclear reactions proper.

In all experiments there is a certain probability of each of these processes occurring, which can be measured by counting the number of particles appearing in different directions and comparing this with the number of incident particles. The data thus obtained can be used to verify theoretical predictions.

Sometimes it is not possible to surround the target by detectors such as shown in Fig. 1.1. This is the case when the target is introduced into the same chamber in which the acceleration of the particles takes place, as for instance often occurs in a cyclotron. Use has then to be made of the fact that the products of nuclear reactions are generally chemically different from the element constituting the target. Consider, for example, the production of radioactive iodine by bombardment of tellurium by deuterons. The nuclear reaction is:

$$_{52}\text{Te}^{130} + \text{d} = {}_{53}\text{I}^{131} + \text{n}$$

The significance of this formula is as follows: a tellurium nucleus consisting of 130 nucleons, of which 52 are protons, is hit by a deuteron; the latter yields a proton to the tellurium and liberates a neutron. A nucleus of iodine consisting of 53 protons and 78 neutrons is formed. The radioactive iodine thus produced may be separated chemically and its activity gives an indication of the number of iodine nuclei obtained. This radioactive iodine has important applications in medicine for the diagnosis and treatment of illnesses of the thyroid gland.

For sufficiently high energies the electromagnetic interaction can often be neglected, since its magnitude is much smaller than the kinetic energy of the incident particle. Similarly, for very energetic incoming particles, the interaction between nucleons inside the nucleus becomes unimportant. For instance, protons of about 200 MeV may induce the so-called spallation reations, in which the nucleus literally explodes into various fragments, formed by the collision of the incident particle with the individual nucleons.

At energies above 300 MeV, which can be obtained with synchrocyclotrons, a new particle appears: the meson. Its existence was predicted theoretically by Yukawa, who postulated that nuclear forces were due to the continuous exchange of mesons between nucleons. The study of cosmic rays and experiments carried out with accelerators have since brilliantly confirmed his theory. The production of mesons can be understood within the framework of the theory of relativity, according to which mass and energy are closely related attributes of matter, so that when two protons collide part of their kinetic energy can reappear in the form of mass of a third particle, the meson.

The meson is one of the many new particles discovered during the last quarter of a century. Previously, the ultimate constituents of matter appeared to be only three: the proton, the neutron and the electron. In addition, the existence of the positron or positive electron and the photon – a particle of zero mass which accounts for the corpuscular nature of light – had been established. Furthermore, the hypothesis of another particle of zero mass, the neutrino, had been advanced as the only way to account for the conservation of energy during the emission of electrons of both signs by radioactive nuclei.

This relatively simple picture has now become extremely complicated. The mesons found in cosmic radiation have turned out to be unstable, decaying into a positive or negative electron (since there are mesons of both signs) and two neutrinos within an average time of $2 \cdot 15 \times 10^{-6}$ seconds. It was subsequently shown that these particles were not those predicted by Yukawa, but rather what we might call their 'daughter' products. In fact the Yukawa mesons or π-mesons have an even shorter lifetime of 10^{-8} s and on decay produce the μ-mesons found in the cosmic radiation. In addition to π-mesons of positive and negative charge there also exists a neutral pion with a lifetime of 10^{-15} seconds.

Naturally, the accelerators have been important instruments in conducting research concerning these particles. Although cosmic rays have (at least at the moment) the advantage of having higher energies than those obtainable with accelerators, they have the drawback that the scientist cannot control them at will, and that their effects can only be observed after they have traversed a thick atmospheric layer. A synchrocyclotron or a proton synchrotron can on the other hand yield not only protons of high energy but also relatively intense beams of π-mesons, which because of their short lifetime will decay into μ-mesons and neutrinos after having travelled a few metres from the target in which they were formed. These beams provide the tool for the study of a new and interesting field of physics: the investigation of the internal structure of the so-called elementary particles. In fact their proliferation has led to the conclusion that they are not so elementary as they were once thought to be. An example of the complex installations needed to conduct these studies is shown in Fig. 1.3.

If the projectile energy is further increased, a different type of meson can be produced: the K-meson, whose properties are listed in Table 1.2, together with those of other 'elementary' particles. The K-mesons and the even heavier particles called hyperons can only be obtained with the aid of giant accelerators known as synchrotrons.

Accelerators have made possible the materialization of still other kinds of particles, called *antiparticles*, whose existence has not only a profound significance in physics but also cosmological implications. The electron-positron pair is a typical example of the particle-antiparticle relationship: they have opposite charge and magnetic moment, and otherwise similar properties; they are created together by the annihilation of a γ-ray of sufficiently high energy. Although the positron is not a constituent of ordinary matter in the same sense as the electron, once created it is stable except for collisions with other electrons.

The above symmetry between electrons and positrons suggests that other antiparticles may exist. The antiproton should have the same mass as the proton but opposite charge and magnetic moment. The antineutron and the neutron would differ in the signs of their magnetic moments. All these particles have indeed been found, thanks to the Bevatron at Berkeley which is capable of accelerating protons up to energies of 6000 MeV.

These findings open a wide field for speculation. One could think of antimatter, constituted by antiparticles. The antihydrogen, for instance, would be formed by a positron revolving around an antiproton; the antihelium would have two antiprotons and two antineutrons in the nucleus and two positrons on the outside, and so forth. Antimatter would have the inconvenient property of annihilating with ordinary matter, producing radiant energy. This may explain why there is no antimatter in our galaxy, but does not exclude the possibility that outside the range of our telescopes, there may exist antigalaxies in which ordinary matter is forbidden in much the same way as is antimatter in ours. The existence of antigalaxies could provide an explanation for enormous sources of energy capable of producing, for example, cosmic rays by collisions between galaxies and antigalaxies.

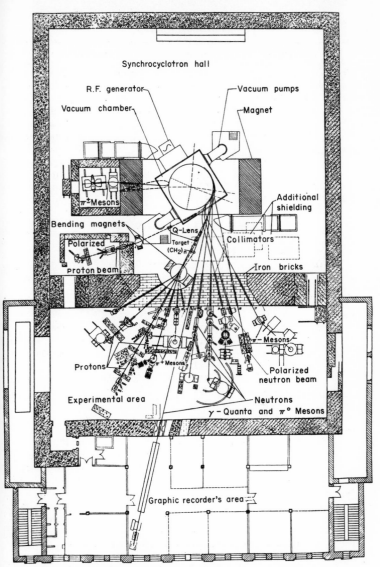

Fig. 1.3. Experimental area of the 660 MeV synchrocyclotron at Dubna (U.S.S.R.). The primary beam produces mesons of different kinds, which are in turn used as projectiles in many experiments. (*By courtesy of the Joint Institute for Nuclear Research*).

TABLE 1.2
Fundamental Particles

| Antiparticles | | Mass | Particles | |
Symbol	Charge	(MeV)	Charge	Symbol
Baryons and antibaryons				
$\bar{\Delta}$	$-2, -1, 0, +1$	1 920	$-1, 0, +1, +2$	Δ (Delta)
$\bar{\Lambda}$	0	1 815	0	Λ (Lambda)
$\bar{N}$	$-1, 0$	1 688	$0, +1$	N (Nucleon)
$\bar{\Omega}$	$+1$	1 676	-1	Ω (omega)
$\bar{\Sigma}$	$-1, 0, +1$	1 660	$-1, 0, +1$	Σ (Sigma)
$\bar{\Xi}$	$0, +1$	1 530	$-1, 0$	Ξ (Xi)
$\bar{\Lambda}$	0	1 520	0	Λ
$\bar{N}$	$-1, 0$	1 512	$0, +1$	N
$\bar{\Lambda}$	0	1 405	0	Λ
$\bar{\Sigma}$	$-1, 0, +1$	1 385	$-1, 0, +1$	Σ
$\bar{\Xi}$	$0, +1$	1 318	$-1, 0$	Ξ
$\bar{\Delta}$	$-2, -1, 0, +1$	1 238	$-1, 0, +1, +2$	Δ
$\bar{\Sigma}$	$-1, 0, +1$	1 193	$-1, 0, +1$	Σ
$\bar{\Lambda}$	0	1 115	0	Λ
$\bar{N}$	$-1, 0$	939	$0, +1$	N
Mesons				
		1 250	0	η (Eta)
		1 020	0	η
$\bar{\kappa}$	$-1, 0$	888	$0, +1$	κ (Kappa)
		782	0	η
		750	$-1, 0, +1$	π (Pi)
$\bar{\kappa}$	$-1, 0$	496	$0, +1$	κ
		137	$-1, 0, +1$	π
Leptons and antileptons				
μ^+	$+1$	106	-1	μ^- (Muon)
e^+	$+1$	0·511	-1	e^- (Electron)
$\bar{\nu}$	$0, 0$	0	$0, 0$	ν (Neutrino)
Photon				
		0	0	γ (Photon or gamma-ray)

The charge of different particles is shown in terms of electronic units. Particles differing only in their charge, but similar in other respects, are designated by the same symbol. A common symbol is also used for recurrences, that is groups of particles with the same charge states [for example, $\Sigma(-1, 0, +1)$] but different masses and values of the intrinsic angular momentum (spin).

Antimatter could also have great practical application. If a process were found by means of which it could be generated under controlled conditions, its annihilation with ordinary matter would provide us with tremendous sources of power by the complete transformation of mass into energy. In order to realize what this means, it should be remembered that in nuclear explosions only a small percentage of nuclear masses is converted into energy.

Thirty types of particles were known by 1957. They were rather simply classified according to their mass. Sixteen heavy particles and antiparticles, such as neutrons, protons, and hyperons, were called baryons and antibaryons (eight of each). In addition, seven mesons (medium-mass particles), three leptons (light particles), three antileptons and the photon were known. Since then it has been shown that there were two kinds of neutrinos, which has increased the list by one lepton and one antilepton. On the other hand, the total number of baryons, antibaryons and mesons has gone up from twenty-three to the rather impressive figure of eighty-two. A realistic classification of these particles is as important for present-day physics as was the Periodic Table of the Elements for chemistry in the last century. Successful, although perhaps not definitive, attempts at such classification have led to the prediction and subsequent discovery of new particles which came to fill existing gaps in the Table. Of course, a classification of the fundamental particles must be based on completely different principles from those underlying the Periodic Table. But the main difference lies in the fact that the chemical elements form a sort of closed system, pre-existent in Nature and finite in number. On the other hand, the question of how many new particles we shall be able to create as higher energy accelerators become available, is still an open one.

CHAPTER 2

Fundamental Principles
of Particle Acceleration

The structure of a particle accelerator can be represented very schematically by a diagram such as that of Fig. 2.1. There are three fundamental components: the ion source or electron gun (according to the type of particle to be accelerated), in which the particles are produced; an

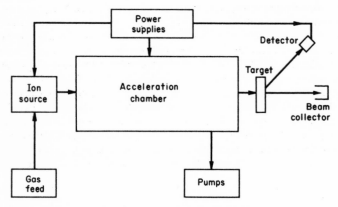

Fig. 2.1. Schematic diagram of a particle accelerator.

acceleration chamber under high vacuum, where the acceleration is performed, and a target on which the high velocity particles impinge. The latter may be surrounded by detectors to observe the products of nuclear interactions in the target.

Besides these basic components some machines require power generators to energize the coils of a large magnet, high-voltage supplies, generators of oscillating electric fields, etc. All these items have been grouped together as power supplies in Fig. 2.1. Vacuum pumps are obviously needed to remove the air from the acceleration chamber, thus allowing the acceleration to proceed unperturbed.

Of all the physical phenomena taking place in such a complex installation, we shall be mainly concerned in this book with those occurring in the acceleration chamber. The processes produced in the target are of a completely different nature, and have been touched upon in the previous chapter.

The acceleration chamber may have widely different shapes in different types of machines, but the physical principles underlying the acceleration of particles are the same in all cases. These principles, namely the laws of mechanical motion and interaction of charged particles with the electromagnetic field, will be the subject of this chapter.

1. Laws of Motion

The word *particle*, as used here, designates those systems whose dimensions are so small compared with the space in which they move that their internal structure and the movements thereof can be neglected when studying the motion of the system as a whole. The earth within the solar system is such a particle, as well as a proton moving inside an accelerator.

The position of a particle in space can be specified by a set of three numbers, the coordinates of the particle in a system of reference. In the cartesian system of coordinates these numbers are the components of a vector, the position vector of the particle. In this book we shall make frequent use of the cylindrical system of coordinates, since it is suitable for the description of the phenomena occurring in many accelerators.

If a particle moves, its position vector will change in magnitude and direction with time. This is expressed mathematically by saying that $\mathbf{r} = \mathbf{r}(t)$ or, in words, the position vector $\mathbf{r}$ is a function of time. The *velocity* of a particle is defined as the rate of change of $\mathbf{r}$ with time. That is to say, if the distance travelled by a particle in time Δt is $\Delta \mathbf{r}$, the mean velocity is the ratio $\Delta \mathbf{r}/\Delta t$, whilst the instantaneous velocity is defined as the limit to which this ratio tends when the interval Δt is made shorter and shorter, approaching the value zero. In symbols,

$$\mathbf{v} = \lim_{\Delta t \to 0} \frac{\Delta \mathbf{r}}{\Delta t} = \frac{d\mathbf{r}}{dt} = \dot{\mathbf{r}} . \tag{2.1}$$

The velocity is the derivative of the vector **r** with respect to time, and is itself a vector. Similarly, the acceleration is the rate of change of velocity with time,

$$\mathbf{a} = \lim_{\Delta t \to 0} \frac{\Delta \mathbf{v}}{\Delta t} = \frac{d\mathbf{v}}{dt} = \dot{\mathbf{v}}, \tag{2.2}$$

and is directed along the increment of velocity d**v** in time dt. It is easy to see that if acceleration and velocity are parallel, the former implies only a change in magnitude, but not in direction, of the latter, while a change in direction not affecting the magnitude is obtained when the velocity and acceleration are normal to each other. The aim of particle accelerators is of course to produce the first type of change in velocity, although the second type is often needed to confine the motion to practical limits.

The problem is then how to produce accelerations. Mechanics has in fact a ready-made answer to this problem: according to the fundamental law of dynamics, due to Newton, a particle of mass m will suffer an acceleration **a** when subjected to a force **F**, all three quantities satisfying the equation:

$$\mathbf{F} = m\mathbf{a}. \tag{2.3}$$

But besides the rather philosophical definition of forces as the most general form of interaction between material bodies, mechanics does not concern itself with the origin of these forces. Nature, anyway, provides us with innumerable examples, such as the nuclear forces which we mentioned in the previous chapter or the electric force which a charged particle exerts on another.

Let us apply the above ideas to a particular case: that of a uniform circular motion. The moon around the earth and an electron inside a synchrotron perform approximately this type of movement, namely that of a particle moving on a circumference with constant speed. Since the direction of motion is continuously changing, the particle must suffer an acceleration, which we shall calculate later on. The time required by the particle to perform a single turn around the circumference is constant and is called the period of revolution. The frequency, defined as the number of revolutions per second, is also constant. This quantity is closely related to the angular velocity, or angle swept by the radius vector in unit time. In fact, the angle swept during one revolution is 2π radians and since the number of revolutions per unit time is the frequency f, the angular velocity is given by

$$\omega = 2\pi f.$$

The linear velocity is the arc length traversed in unit time; since an angle is defined as the ratio of arc length to radius, we obtain for the angular velocity

$$\omega = v/r \ . \tag{2.4}$$

We have said that a change in the direction of the velocity implies an acceleration at right angles to the velocity. In the case of circular motion this is called centripetal acceleration, since it is directed along the radius vector toward the centre of the circle. Its magnitude can be obtained by observing that the angular rate of change of the velocity vector is the same as that of the radius vector, that is, the angular velocity ω. The change in velocity dv in a short interval of time dt is then the arc traced by the end of the velocity vector on a circle of radius v over the angle ωdt. The length of this arc is

$$dv = v\omega dt \ ,$$

so that the centripetal acceleration is

$$\mathbf{a} = (dv/dt) = v\omega = \omega^2 r = v^2/r \ . \tag{2.5}$$

So far we have obtained the magnitude of the acceleration by means of geometrical arguments. But the actual physical process requires the presence of a centripetal force, perpendicular to the velocity, as that provided by the attraction of the earth on the moon or by the magnetic field of a synchrotron on an electron. Given the force, the mass and the velocity of the particle, the resulting trajectory will be a circumference whose radius will satisfy the fundamental law of dynamics in the form

$$\mathbf{F} = m\mathbf{a} = mv^2/r \ .$$

Circular motion is interesting also in connexion with the so-called harmonic motion, which describes for example the oscillations of a weight suspended from a spring. Let P' be the projection on a diameter of a point P on the circumference. As P moves, sweeping an angle φ from 0 to 2π, P' performs harmonic oscillations, going from the centre to one end of the diameter, then to the other end and back to the centre. The distance between P' and the centre is called elongation, and its maximum value $(=r)$ is the amplitude. The elongation at time t is given by $r \sin \varphi = r \sin \omega t$. All quantities pertaining to circular motion have their counterpart in harmonic motion: the angular velocity corresponds to the circular frequency ω, the angle φ is the phase. The words 'frequency' and 'period' are retained, meaning now number of oscillations per unit time and time required for one oscillation, respectively.

In our study of accelerators we shall make use of quantities (voltage, electric and magnetic fields, etc) which vary with time in exactly the same way as the elongation of harmonic motion. The same concepts of frequency, phase, etc, can be applied to such cases.

2. Energy and Work

The fundamental law of dynamics refers to the *instantaneous* effects of forces. If a force $\mathbf{F} = \mathbf{F}(t)$, whose magnitude and orientation depend upon the time, is applied to a particle of mass m initially at rest, its effect can be obtained by integrating the equation of motion,

$$\int_0^t \mathbf{F}(t)\mathrm{d}t = \int_0^t m\mathbf{a}\,\mathrm{d}t = m\mathbf{v}\,, \qquad (2.6)$$

since $\mathbf{a}\mathrm{d}t = \mathrm{d}\mathbf{v}$. The quantity $m\mathbf{v}$ is called the *momentum* of the particle.

If we now turn our attention to the *work* performed by a force, we shall have to calculate the integral $\int \mathbf{F}\mathrm{d}\mathbf{r}$, where the two vectors $\mathbf{F}$ and $\mathrm{d}\mathbf{r}$ form a scalar product. This can be done as follows:

$$\int_{r_0}^r \mathbf{F}.\mathrm{d}\mathbf{r} = \int_{r_0}^r \mathbf{F}.\frac{\mathrm{d}\mathbf{r}}{\mathrm{d}t}\,\mathrm{d}t = \int_{r_0}^r m\mathbf{a}.\mathbf{v}\mathrm{d}t = \int_{r_0}^r m\mathbf{v}.\mathrm{d}\mathbf{v} = \tfrac{1}{2}mv^2 - \tfrac{1}{2}mv_0^2 \quad (2.7)$$

where $\mathbf{v}$ is the velocity at point $\mathbf{r}$ and $\mathbf{v}_0$ the velocity at point $\mathbf{r}_0$. The quantity $\tfrac{1}{2}mv^2$ is the *kinetic energy* of the particle, and the relation obtained is just a particular case of the general theorem of conservation of energy: the work performed by external forces on a particle (the integral in the left-hand side) is equal to the change in its kinetic energy (the right-hand side).

Of course, a force perpendicular to the trajectory does not work at all, since then the scalar product $\mathbf{F}.\mathrm{d}\mathbf{r} = 0$; this is the case of the circular motion described above, where the centripetal force produces no variation of the kinetic energy. This also applies to the forces exerted by magnetic fields on moving charged particles, as we shall see later.

3. Relativistic Motion

Our description up to now does not extend beyond the limits of classical, prerelativistic mechanics, which is valid as long as the velocities implied are small compared with that of light (300 000 km/s). But the particles obtained from accelerators – and this is particularly true of electrons – may have velocities practically indistinguishable from that of light. We shall need, therefore, at least some of the fundamental conclusions of the theory of relativity.

According to the theory of relativity, a moving body cannot acquire a velocity greater than that of light in free space. This is fundamentally different from classical mechanics, where no such limit exists.

Up to now, we have considered the mass of a particle to be a constant, independent of the state of motion. This is no longer true in relativistic mechanics, where the mass increases with the particle velocity, according to the law

$$m = \frac{m_0}{\sqrt{[1 - (v/c)^2]}}, \qquad (2.8)$$

where c is the velocity of light and m_0 is called the rest mass of the particle (value of m for which $v = 0$), equivalent to the mass of classical mechanics. The increase of mass with velocity is shown in Fig. 2.2, in which it can be

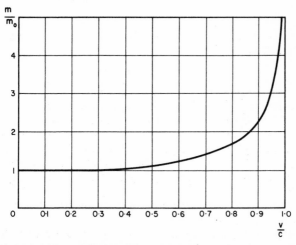

Fig. 2.2. Mass of a particle depending on its velocity. The mass variation is negligible up to about 60 000 km/s ($v = 0.2c$), where it is only 2 per cent, but becomes important at higher velocities.

seen that the mass tends to an infinite value when v approaches the value c, thus making any further acceleration impossible if finite forces are applied. This is in complete agreement with the notion of c as an upper limit to any velocity.

The theory also establishes a relationship between mass and energy: any increase in energy brings about a proportional increase in mass, the coefficient of proportionality being c^2. If a particle initially at rest acquires the kinetic energy T, its mass will change from m_0 to m, according to the equation

$$T = mc^2 - m_0 c^2 .$$

This close association between mass and energy makes it natural to define the rest energy as that corresponding to the rest mass,

$$W_0 = m_0 c^2 ,$$

and the total energy as

$$W = W_0 + T = mc^2 = \frac{m_0 c^2}{\sqrt{(1 - \beta^2)}} , \qquad (2.9)$$

where $\beta = v/c$.

From the above equations a relation between total energy and momentum can be obtained,

$$W^2 = W_0^2 + (mv)^2 c^2 , \qquad (2.10)$$

of which we shall make use later on in this book.

The relativistic effects become important when the quantity $(1 - \beta^2)^{-\frac{1}{2}} = W/W_0$ differs appreciably form unity, that is to say, when the total energy is large compared with the rest energy. This is the reason why, as shown in Fig.2.3, those effects appear in electrons of relatively low kinetic energies, their rest energy being only 0·51 MeV. Protons, which are 1836 times heavier, become fully relativistic only at the highest energies attained at present.

Three more or less distinct energy regions can be defined, according to the kinetic energy of the particles:

(1) *Low energies,* extending up to about 15 keV for electrons and 30 MeV for protons. The mass remains practically constant, and all the formulae of classical mechanics are valid.

(2) *Intermediate energies,* for which the mass variation becomes in-

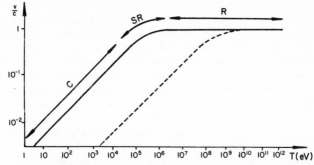

Fig. 2.3. Electron velocity (solid line) and proton velocity (dashed line) as functions of kinetic energy. The regions shown correspond to: validity of classical mechanics (C), semirelativistic transition region (SR) and fully relativistic region (R).

creasingly important, although the classical formulae can be used when suitable correction terms are added. This domain is called semirelativistic, and covers the energy range from 15 keV to 2 MeV in the case of electrons and from 30 MeV to 4000 MeV (4 GeV) for protons.

(3) *High energies*: the particle has practically reached the velocity of light. Successive 'accelerations' do not bring about a discernible change in velocity, but new mass increments instead. Only relativistic equations may be used.

4. Interaction of Charged Particles with the Electromagnetic Field

Up to this point we have referred to forces and their effects without mentioning the origin of the forces acting on ions and electrons. These particles possess electric charge and are therefore subject to the influence of the electric and magnetic fields created by other charges. This property lies at the very heart of our study, since one might define the art of particle acceleration as the search for ingenious combinations of electric and magnetic fields in order to produce large energy gains in a limited region of space at minimum cost.

Although the existence of electric charges in matter has been known since Greek antiquity, it was only in 1785 that Coulomb could describe quantitatively the interaction between point charges. His measurements showed that two charges exert upon one another a force proportional to their intensities and inversely proportional to the square of the distance between them. This force is directed along the line joining both charges, and is repulsive or attractive depending on whether they are of the same or different sign. Actually, the assignment of sign is purely conventional, since no experiment tells which charge is to be called positive and which one negative. Coulomb's experiments made another point clear, namely that charges could interact at a distance, without being in actual contact. Further work by Faraday and Maxwell allowed a more rigourous definition of *electric field*. According to their ideas the space surrounding a charge or distribution of charges is modified in such a way that it has the property of exerting a force on any new charge introduced in the region. Charges project themselves, as it were, beyond their perceptible limits through this modification of space called electric field.

The force acting on a charge in the field is proportional to the charge itself. The field intensity is defined as the force acting on the unit of charge and, like force, is a vector whose magnitude and direction can in principle be specified for every point in space.

Let us now consider a charged particle moving under the action of an electric field. The field forces will do a certain work during the movement and, according to what we said above, the particle will gain the corresponding kinetic energy. The work done may equivalently be thought of as energy stored in the field. This energy can be *potentially* given up by the field and is therefore called potential energy, or simply potential when referred to the positive unit of charge. Any two points in a field can be the end-points of a trajectory: a particle with q units of charge will gain (or lose, according to the sign of the charge) the kinetic energy

$$\Delta T = q \Delta V, \tag{2.11}$$

where ΔV is called the potential difference or voltage between both points. This is precisely the method used in all present accelerators to increase the kinetic energy of charged particles: they travel between two points at different potential.

There exist certain substances—metals in particular—in which the electric charges can move with almost absolute freedom*. These sub-

---

* 'Electric charges' here stand for the specific charge carriers (generally electrons) of the metal in question. A low-energy proton, for instance, is almost immediately brought to rest and trapped in the crystalline lattice.

stances are called *conductors*. Conducting bodies placed in an electrostatic field (that is, one in which the charges do not move) possess the property of having all their points at the same potential. For if a potential difference existed between two points in a conductor the resulting electric field would make the charges flow, negative charges accumulating at the point of highest potential. The flowing charges would thus tend to create an additional field opposing the initial one, and the flow would cease only when both fields cancelled each other. In other words, unless an external source of electromotive force is applied, capable of removing the flowing charges and thus maintaining the potential difference, no permanent electric field can exist in a conductor.

This property of conductors allows the 'shaping' of electric fields according to particular needs. In fact, the electric field at the surface of a conductor must be perpendicular to that surface (otherwise the tangential component of the field would bring about a flow of charges, and the same reasoning as above applies). If a line is drawn starting from a point at the surface of a conductor and such that it is always tangent to the electric field vector, it will be found that the line either extends to infinity or ends on another conductor at a different potential. Such an imaginary line is called a 'line of force'. Although the lines of force do not necessarily coincide with the possible trajectories of particles moving in the field, they show qualitatively how the field may be expected to influence the paths. We shall make use of this fact when referring to focussing effects in particle accelerators.

We shall be concerned with still another quantity, namely the *capacity*. This is simply the ratio of the charge in a conductor to its voltage with respect to surrounding conductors. The 'surrounding conductors' may be the walls and floor of a room, or massive metallic equipment near the conductor, commonly referred to as ground or earth potential and conventionally defined as having zero potential. When charges are forced into a conductor insulated from earth, its potential increases according to the equation

$$V = q/C \,,$$

where C, the capacity, is a constant depending on the shape of the conductor and its proximity to other conductors. The operation of the Van de Graaff generator, to be described in Chapter 3, is based upon these facts.

The fields we have considered up to now did not vary with time.

Particle accelerators, however, make use of variable fields, particularly of those undergoing periodic variations. Harmonic oscillations, entirely similar to the mechanical oscillations mentioned earlier, are also present here. An alternating voltage of frequency f will be represented by

$$V = V_{max} \sin\left(2\,\pi f t + \varphi_0\right), \qquad (2.12)$$

where φ_0 is the phase at time $t=0$, and V_{max} is the maximum possible value of V

Electric fields are not the only means of acting on charged particles. Moving charges are also affected by magnetic fields, suffering a force perpendicular to both the velocity and the field, as shown in Fig. 2.4. On

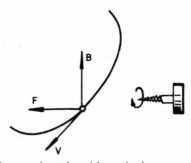

Fig. 2.4. Force acting on a charged particle moving in a magnetic field. The force is perpendicular to both the velocity and the field and is directed along the line of advance of a corkscrew which rotates from **v** to **B**.

the other hand, moving charges constitute electric currents, and the sources of magnetic fields can always be found in such currents. In the case of permanent magnets, the magnetic field originates in the microscopic currents produced by atomic electrons revolving in their orbits. In electromagnets, the primary source of the field is the current flowing through a coil wound around an iron core. The field produced by this current aligns the microscopic currents in the iron, which in turn produce the required field. The force exerted by a magnetic field on a moving charge is given by the vector equation

$$\mathbf{F} = q\mathbf{v} \times \mathbf{B}, \qquad (2.13)$$

where **F** is the force, q the particle's charge, **v** its velocity and **B** is a vector called magnetic induction or flux density, which characterizes the field. The vector product $\mathbf{v} \times \mathbf{B}$ implies that the direction of the force will be that shown in Fig. 2.4 and that its intensity will be

$$F = qvB \sin \theta \, ,$$

where θ is the angle formed by $\mathbf{v}$ and $\mathbf{B}$. Another way of looking at this is to consider that the component of $\mathbf{B}$ along $\mathbf{v}$ (or conversely, the component of $\mathbf{v}$ along $\mathbf{B}$) does not influence the movement, and that the normal component $B \sin \theta$ (or $v \sin \theta$) is the only one contributing to the force. We shall often make use of this point of view when expressing our equations.

Since the force exerted by a magnetic field on a moving particle is perpendicular to the velocity and hence to the trajectory, it will do no work, and consequently no energy gain will result from it. It would seem that magnetic fields are useless from the point of view of particle acceleration, but this is not true; in fact, the magnetic force (or Lorentz force, as it is also called) bends trajectories which would be otherwise rectilinear. Particles in a suitable field describe a closed path, and the dimensions of the machine which has to accommodate the trajectories can thus be considerably reduced. This is the basis of the operation of circular accelerators, to be described in Chapter 5 and subsequent chapters.

Let us consider a particle moving initially at right angles to a constant magnetic field. If there is no accelerating electric field the velocity will be constant in absolute value, and so will be the force (perpendicular to the trajectory) acting on the particle. These are just the conditions for uniform circular motion, which is indeed the resulting motion. The formulae already given apply. The force will be related to the velocity and the circle radius r by

$$F = qvB = mv^2/r \, ,$$

from which the angular velocity is obtained as

$$\omega = v/r = qB/m \, . \tag{2.14}$$

In the non-relativistic region, where the mass can be considered constant, the angular velocity does not depend on the energy. At very high energies, in the relativistic region, the same equation is valid, although it may be useful to replace it by

$$\omega = qBc^2/W, \tag{2.15}$$

which results from the relativistic relationship between the mass and the total energy.

The *magnetic rigidity* of a particle is the product

$$Br = mv/q ,\qquad (2.16)$$

i.e., the momentum divided by the charge; particles of small momentum move on circumferences of smaller radii (in other words, they are less 'rigid') than those of higher momentum in the same magnetic field.

The forces that a magnetostatic field exerts on a charged particle do no work, as we have seen. This is no longer true when the field varies with time. In such a case an electric field appears, whose intensity depends on the rate of variation of the magnetic field. This fact is basic for the acceleration of electrons in machines such as the betatron and synchrotron. On the other hand, the operation of the well-known voltage transformer depends on the same phenomenon.

In order to gain further insight into the generation of this electric field we shall have to define the notion of magnetic flux. Referring to Fig. 2.5

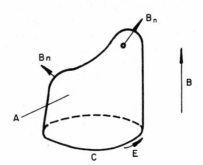

Fig. 2.5. Magnetic flux through a surface A bounded by a contour C.

let us consider a surface A bounded by a contour C. The magnetic flux, or flux of the vector **B** through this surface is

$$\Phi = \int_A B_n \mathrm{d}A ,\qquad (2.17)$$

where B_n is the component of the field perpendicular to the surface at every point on it. It would seem at first sight that if the surface were deformed like a soap film on a wire frame, the value of the integral defining the flux would change; but the flux density belongs to a class of vectors called solenoidal, for which the flux is constant, whatever the shape of the surface, as long as the contour and the field remain the same. We might as well have taken the piece of plane surface on which the contour C lies in Fig. 2.5. Now, if the magnetic field varies, an electric field E will appear distributed along the contour, corresponding to a potential difference

$$V = -\frac{\mathrm{d}\Phi}{\mathrm{d}t} = \oint \mathbf{E}.\mathrm{d}\mathbf{r} \,. \qquad (2.18)$$

The integral on the right is, according to the definitions of work and electric field, nothing but the work done on the unit positive charge when describing the closed contour. We are then justified in equating it to a potential difference. It may be worth noting that in the electrostatic case a potential difference can be established between two *different* points in space independently of the path joining them. On the other hand, the potential difference resulting from Faraday's law, as the above equation is called, depends upon the path described. The unit of charge, returning to the *same* point after describing a closed contour, will gain a kinetic energy given by eqn. (2.18).

We have been dealing with ideal contours and surfaces. What happens in practice if an electron is allowed to move in an increasing magnetic field? Under the influence of the field its trajectory will become a closed path, corresponding to one of those ideal contours. As long as the field increases, every round trip on this sort of orbit will mean an energy gain for the electron. This is the principle of operation of the betatron, which we shall study in detail in Chapter 5.

5. Units and Dimensions

The formulae we have written down only become valid once a certain system of units has been agreed upon. In this book we shall adhere (with minor exceptions) to the mks system of units, in which the metre (m), the kilogram (kg) and the second (s) are the fundamental units of length, mass and time, respectively. A fundamental unit of electric charge, the coulomb, is added to these mechanical units, and from the four of them all derived units follow, as we shall outline below.

The unit of force (the newton) will be that force which applied to a mass of 1 kg brings about an acceleration of 1 m/s^2. The work done by this force along 1 m will be the unit of work (or energy), the joule. The potential difference between two points will be unity (one volt) if the work done by the electric forces in displacing a charge of one coulomb from one point to the other is one joule.

The particles used in accelerators have either the charge of the electron ($1 \cdot 602 \times 10^{-19}$ coulombs) or an integral multiple of it. It is natural to take this as the unit of charge, and to replace the joule (1 coulomb × 1 volt) by the electron-volt, i.e., the energy gained (or lost) by an electron when traversing a potential difference of one volt. We have then:

1 eV (electron-volt) = $1 \cdot 602 \times 10^{-19}$ joules

1 keV (kiloelectron-volt) = 1 000 eV

1 MeV (megaelectron-volt) = 10^6 eV

1 GeV (gigaelectron-volt, in Europe) or 1 BeV (bevaelectron-volt, in the U.S.A.) = 10^9 eV.

Of course, when saying that the kinetic energy of a proton is 100 MeV, for example, one does not necessarily mean that it has passed through a potential difference of 100 million volts, but that its energy, independently of the way in which it has been acquired, is $1 \cdot 602 \times 10^{-19} \times 10^8 = 1 \cdot 602 \times 10^{-11}$ joule.

The farad, unit of capacity, is defined as the capacity of a conducting body whose potential will be raised 1 volt by a charge of 1 coulomb. This is a rather large unit; the capacity of the earth, for example, is less than 10^{-3} farad. The microfarad ($= 10^{-6}$ farad) is of more general use.

The unit of electric current is the ampere, which corresponds to a flow of one coulomb per second. The range of electric currents used in accelerators is tremendous, going from thousands of amperes in the coils of the electromagnets of certain machines to thousandths of microamperes (10^{-9} amperes) in the beam of particles finally produced.

The unit of magnetic flux is the weber, and that of flux density is the weber/m². The gauss (1 gauss = 10^{-4} weber/m²) is very commonly employed, and we shall make frequent use of it, although it does not belong to the mks system of units. The field between the pole tips of a small permanent magnet may be of about 200 gauss, although magnets made of special steel reach fields of 2 000 gauss. Electromagnets with iron cores produce fields of up to 20 000 gauss, a limit beyond which the best practicable steels reach saturation, i.e., further increases in the coil current do not bring about a proportional increase in the field.

CHAPTER 3

Static Accelerators

In the previous chapter we examined the fundamental principles upon which particle acceleration is based. The present one will be devoted to a particular application of these principles: that of machines where the ions or electrons move along straight paths and the fields used for acceleration are constant in time. Magnetic fields must of course be absent, since their components normal to the velocity would produce a certain curvature of the trajectory.

Charged particles are accelerated whenever subjected to the action of an electric field. After traversing a potential difference of V volts, a particle with charge Z times that of the electron, will have a kinetic energy of ZV electron volts. It would seem that the simplest way of attaining the desired energy gain would be to make the particles travel through the corresponding potencial drop. But the voltages involved are so high that common generators are not suitable at all. For example, if an alpha-particle $(Z = 2)$ is to surmount the barrier represented by the electrostatic repulsion of an iron nucleus in order to unleash a nuclear reaction, it must have an energy of 13 MeV. There exist quite a few generators producing potential differences in the million-volt range. Two of them, the Van de Graaff and the Cockcroft-Walton generators have been in use for many years as particle accelerators. A third, the insulating core transformer, is of more recent appearance. To these machines we now turn our attention.

1. The Electrostatic Van de Graaff Generator; Principles of Operation

The Van de Graaff machine can deliver very high voltages by mechanically driving charges into a conductor. Let us recall that, according to what we said in Chapter 2, the total charge Q in a conductor and its voltage V with respect to other conductors are related by the expression

$$V = Q/C \tag{3.1}$$

where C, the capacity of the system, depends solely upon the geometrical distribution of conductors and the dielectric properties of the insulators. The meaning of this equation is twofold: on the one hand it implies the appearance of a charge Q on the surface of the conductor whenever its voltage is raised to the value V. On the other, it tells us that the voltage will take that value whenever the charge Q is forced into the conductor. The means by which the charge is carried is in principle immaterial. The

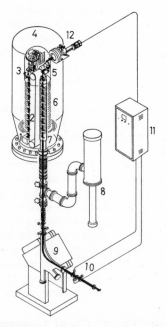

Fig. 3.1. Sketch of a Van de Graaff accelerator.
(1) D. C. power supply. (2) Insulating belt. (3) High-voltage terminal. (4) Pressurized tank with insulating gas. (5) Ion source. (6) Acceleration tube and field-equalizing ring electrodes. (7) Accelerated ion beam. (8) Vacuum pumps. (9) Magnet providing deflection and energy analysis of the beam. (10) Split slit system providing differential signal for energy regulation. (11) Differential signal amplifier. (12) Corona points. (High Voltage Engineering Corporation, Burlington, Massachusetts).

distinctive feature of the Van de Graaff generator is that it uses a conveyor belt for this purpose. Fig. 3.1 illustrates schematically the principle of operation: electric charge is sprayed onto an insulating belt by a corona discharge from an array of needles connected to a d.c. power supply at a few kilovolts. The belt is driven by a motor through a system of two pulleys, carrying the charge into a high-voltage electrode, usually cylindrical with a hemispherical cap. A system of brushes inside this electrode removes the charge from the belt, transferring it to the electrode itself.

It would seem, according to eqn. (3.1), that the potential of the high-voltage terminal would continue to increase as long as charge continues to be transferred to it from the moving belt. This is indeed the case at the beginning of operation, but once the desired voltage has been reached it must be kept fixed by withdrawing the charge at the same rate as it arrives at the high-voltage terminal. Charge removal is performed by a variety of means. First, the accelerated beam itself, leaving the ion source located inside the high-voltage electrode, carries away some of the charge conveyed by the belt. Secondly, insulators are never perfect, so that a certain current will always leak through them back to ground. Some leakage is also due to a steady corona discharge from points at high potential; and finally, a high-resistance voltage divider, usually connected between the terminal and ground, draws some current from the former. A steady state is reached when the rate at which charge is delivered by the belt equals the total current drained. Now, the charge in the belt can, to a certain extend, be modified at will. Also, the current losses mentioned above can be kept under control (for example, the corona discharge is generally used to regulate the magnitude of the high voltage). But even if the charge supply suffices to overcome all forms of drain, the total voltage generated is limited by another factor, namely sparks from the high-voltage electrode.

The spark is the most serious source of troubles in the operation of Van de Graaff generators. As is well known, in any gas there exists a very small quantity of ions of either sign. When an electric field is established, they are accelerated according to their charge, until they lose their energy through collisions with neutral molecules. The corona discharge operates through this mechanism, allowing the ions to drift towards the electrode of sign opposite to their own where they are neutralized. If the field is further increased a condition may be reached in which the energy gained by the ions when travelling the distance between two successive collisions (the mean free path) is enough to produce the ionization of a molecule, i.e., a few electron-volts. In this way each ion produces a few more, which in turn generate more and more, until either the gas is fully ionized or the voltage drops well below the value it had. The latter would be the case in a Van de Graaff machine, since the spark, as the phenomenon is called, would readily exhaust the charge available. Stable operation can only be achieved below the limit set by sparks.

The sparking field in dry air at atmospheric pressure is known by experiment to be 30 kV/cm or, in mks units, 3×10^6 V/m. On the other hand, the field at the surface of a conductor is always perpendicular to it and proportional to the surface density of charge σ. Using mks units,

$$E = \sigma/\varepsilon , \tag{3.2}$$

where ε is the dielectric constant of the medium surrounding the conductor. It this medium is vacuum or air, $\varepsilon = \varepsilon_0 = 10^{-9}/(36\pi)$ farad/m. For a conducting sphere the charge density is given by

$$\sigma = \frac{(\text{total charge})}{(\text{area})} = \frac{Q}{4\pi R^2} , \tag{3.3}$$

where R is the radius of the spherical conductor. Similarly, the potential of the sphere, assuming that all other conductors are infinitely far away, is

$$V = Q/(4\pi\varepsilon R) . \tag{3.4}$$

From eqns. (3.2), (3.3) and (3.4) a relation between the field and the voltage can be worked out, namely,

$$E = V/R \tag{3.5}$$

By setting E equal to the disruptive field (30 kV/cm in atmospheric air) the maximum voltage attainable with an electrode of given dimensions can be found. For example, a one-metre radius sphere operating in the atmosphere would, according to formula (3.5), withstand up to three million volts. In practice, however, generators are usually run at voltages of about one third the theoretical limit.

2. Design Features of Van de Graaff Accelerators

Early Van de Graaff generators, (Van de Graaff, 1931), built in the mid-thirties, were installed inside big sheds. The high-voltage electrode was mounted on insulating columns, and the room size was determined by the need to make the spark path to ground, walls and ceiling as long as possible. As higher and higher voltages were required, it was soon realized that an alternative to ever increasing size had to be found. The replacement of atmospheric air by high-pressure gases (generally nitrogen, freon or a mixture of both) and the large room by a relatively small pressurized tank, provided the clue. In fact, as pressure in a gas increases, the distance between molecules grows correspondingly shorter, and so does the mean free path of an ion. This means that the spark will appear at higher fields, and this is indeed the case: dry nitrogen at 16 atmospheres, for example, can withstand voltage gradients as high as 200 kV/cm without electric breakdown. The straightforward conclusion is that the generator's dimensions can be reduced almost sevenfold with respect to a machine operating at the same voltage in the atmosphere. A five-million-volt generator, for example, can be typically enclosed in a tank 2·5 m in diameter. The machine can thus be horizontally mounted, an alternative not available in the case of generators operating in the atmosphere.

A Van de Graaff accelerator consists, then, of three main parts: the pressurized tank, the generator (driving motor, power supply, moving belt, high-voltage electrode, etc.) and the accelerator proper, that is, the ion source and the acceleration tube. In a negative generator an electron gun would replace the ion source. Whichever the case, the electron gun or ion source must be located inside the high-voltage terminal. Since these devices need some electric power to operate, they are usually fed by a small generator driven by the same belt conveying the charge. The space available inside the terminal is thus made rather restricted, which is a hindrance for the installation of more complicated equipment, as is necessary, for example, for the production of heavy ions such as nuclei of C^{12}. We shall see later on how the so-called tandem accelerators have helped to solve this problem.

As to the acceleration tube, it has to stand the whole potential drop from the high-voltage terminal to ground. The tube is therefore made up of insulating rings separated by metal electrodes, which serve the purpose of providing a gradual voltage drop (they are connected to different points of the aforementioned voltage divider) and ensure that proper focussing (i.e., constriction of the beam to as small a cross-section as possible) is achieved. The question of focussing, fundamental to all types of accelerators, will be dealt with below.

In order to avoid sparks and other forms of current leakage the voltage gradient must be kept to a minimum everywhere. In particular, the field along the belt and the tube must be practically uniform. For this purpose the whole structure is enclosed inside a sort of cage made up of equally spaced metal circular rings having the same outside diameter as the high-voltage electrode. The rings are connected to the voltage divider in such a way that the voltage difference between any two neighbouring rings is the same, thereby ensuring a smooth voltage decrease down to ground.

From what has been said one would expect that the dimensions of Van de Graaff machines would increase roughly linearly with the ultimate voltage desired. In fact, the field along the tube is determined by the spacing between focussing electrodes and their potential difference. Of course, the same applies to the outer rings and, since the field cannot exceed a certain value, higher voltages could only be attained at the cost of increasing proportionally the number of electrodes and circular rings, and therefore the total length of the tube. Unfortunately, early experience showed that the linear relationship did not hold. On the contrary, tube length had to increase at a much faster rate than the voltages obtained, up to a point (about 7 MV) where longer tubes did not result in any practical increase in the voltage. Conversely, this 'total voltage effect', as it is called, shows itself in a given accelerator as a non-linear increase in the voltage with the current delivered to the belt (see Fig. 3.3). Several explanations have been advanced for this phenomenon. One of them assumes that secondary electrons released by particles striking the walls, edges of defining apertures or molecules of residual gas, are accelerated back to hit the positive high-voltage terminal, producing x-rays. The x-rays in turn partially ionize the insulating gas, creating free charges whose removal implies an additional load on the belt. As the voltage and thereby the electron energy increase, more and more penetrating x-rays are produced, with a correspondingly higher yield of ions in the gas, until saturation is ultimately reached.

An ingenious solution to the problem of electron backstreaming has recently been found (Van de Graaff, Rose and Wittkower, 1962) which may completely eliminate the total voltage effect. The usual tubes with electrodes perpendicular to the tube axis have been replaced by 'inclined field tubes' (see Fig. 3.2) which introduce a radial component of the electric field. The length of the electric lines of force is reduced to only a fraction of the total length of the tube. In other words, an electron moving along a line of force will strike an electrode before reaching full energy.

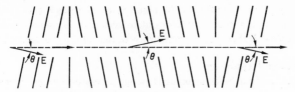

Fig. 3.2. Geometrical arrangement of plane electrodes in inclined field tubes for charged particles. (After Van de Graaff *et al.*, 1962).

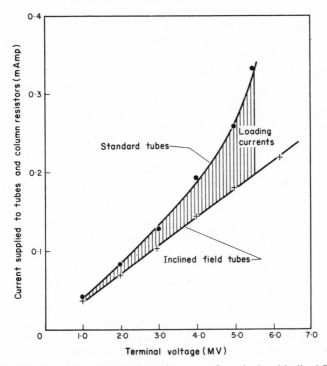

Fig. 3.3. Comparison between the performance of standard and inclined-field tubes. In both cases the same beam current was accelerated. The shaded region shows the current associated with the total voltage effect in standard tubes. (After Van de Graaff *et al.*, 1962).

The inclination of the field is alternately reversed, in such a way that its effect on the ion beam averages out to zero. Fig. 3.3 shows how the performance of these tubes compares with that of the standard ones.

3. Voltage Regulation

Van de Graaff machines are unique among accelerators for their simplicity and ease of operation. Furthermore, they are unrivalled for the accuracy with which the beam energy can be controlled. This is very easily done with the help of the equipment shown in Fig. 3.1. The beam leaving the machine is deflected by a constant magnetic field which, according to eqn. (2.16) will bend the beam into a circle of radius proportional to the velocity. Particles with different energies, therefore, will have different paths inside the magnet. A slit located in the beam path after the magnet allows only the particles with the required energy to go through. Those with higher energy, having suffered a smaller deflection, will hit one side of the slit, whereas the lower energy particles will hit the other. The difference between the currents received by both sides provides an 'error signal', indicating how much the beam is off-centre (and therefore how much off-energy). This signal is amplified and fed into an electron tube which regulates the current drained from the generator by corona points, also indicated in Fig. 3.1. In this way, if the energy is, for example, too high, the current drain is made to increase, thereby making the voltage to drop until the energy reaches the required value. The reverse process takes place if the energy is too low.

How accurate can a given energy setting be? It is clear that this will depend upon the width of the slit (which determines the range of energies allowed to pass) and the constancy in time of the deflecting magnetic field. The latter can be electronically regulated to one part in ten thousand, which is a typical figure for the best energy regulation attainable.

4. Tandem Accelerators

For many years conventional Van de Graaff accelerators could not be operated at voltages higher than 8 MV because of the above-mentioned total voltage effect. This is a fundamental drawback since, as a glance at Fig. 1.2 will show, about half the possible targets in the Periodic Table are beyond the practical limits set to scattering experiments by coulomb barrier effects at that energy. It is only natural that physicists should seek to extend the advantages of the energy regulation and stability characteristic of the Van de Graaff machine to study the heaviest nuclei. The idea of two-stage acceleration originated to serve this aim. In the conventional, single-stage accelerator positive ions are produced inside the high-voltage terminal and subsequently accelerated to ground potential. In the case of two-stage operation, negative ions (that is, atoms to which an additional electron has been attached) are produced at ground potential and accelerated towards the positive terminal. There the electrons are stripped off, and the remaining positive ions proceed again to ground potential, thereby suffering an additional acceleration. The same voltage is thus used twice.

The principle of two-stage acceleration is an old one; its origin can be traced back to the mid-thirties (Bennett and Darby, 1936). But it was only in early 1959 that the first 12-MeV tandem accelerator was put in operation at the Chalk River Laboratories of the Atomic Energy of Canada Ltd. (Van de Graaff, 1960). In 1960 two vertical tandems were installed at the Aldermaston and Harwell laboratories in the United Kingdom, and a third was built in the U.S.S.R. By 1964, more than thirty of these machines were already installed or under construction.

The operation of a two-stage tandem is schematically illustrated in Fig. 3.4. Although any ion source will usually yield a small fraction of negative ions, they are seldom the ones to be accelerated. Instead, positive

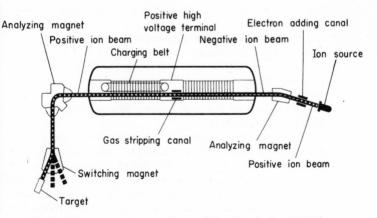

Fig. 3.4. Two-stage tandem accelerator. (After Van de Graaff, 1960).

ions are produced first and are made to impinge at low energy (about 13 keV) onto a charge-exchange canal containing gas at low pressure. There they pick up one or two electrons, in the latter case becoming negative ions. The negative ion beam is then separated from unwanted neutral and positive particles by means of a magnet and directed towards the accelerator proper. The reason for this rather involved procedure is that very intense sources of positive ions are available. The small fraction (about 1 per cent) that leaves the charge-exchange canal as a negative beam suffices to feed the accelerator. In the high-voltage terminal the negative ions traverse a second gas canal, or a very thin carbon foil. Their energy is already a few MeV, much higher than that required to remove the most tightly bound electrons in an atom. Practically all of them, therefore, loose *all* their surrounding electrons, and proceed to the second stage of acceleration as bare nuclei. This implies that when heavy ions are accelerated the second stage is extremely powerful. Take for example oxygen nuclei $(Z = 8)$ and a terminal voltage of 6 million volts. In the first stage they are singly charged, having one electron too many, and gain 6 MeV. But in the second stage they have eight positive charges, thereby acquiring 48 MeV. The final energy adds up to a total of 54 MeV.

The next step is the three-stage tandem shown in Fig. 3.5. The negative ions are formed, not in a source at ground potential, but inside the negative terminal of a conventional Van de Graaff accelerator. They suffer there a first stage of acceleration, and proceed afterwards to a two-stage tandem such as the one described above. This arrangement lacks the advantage of having the ion source at ground potential, which is one of the most interesting features of two-stage tandems. In fact, a ground potential ion source means accessibility, ample room for the installation of massive equipment required for the production of heavy ions and simplicity in the switching over from one type of equipment to another. Moreover, certain elements, like helium, do not form negative ions, which precludes the acceleration of alpha-particles.

The ion source can be brought back to ground potential operation by use of the neutral beam injection technique, illustrated in Fig. 3.6. Positive ions, as in two-stage operation, enter an electron-adding canal. In this case, however, the negative beam is not sought but rather the large fraction (up to 90%) of particles, which results in the formation of neutral atoms by the addition of a single electron. The neutral beam proceeds to the negative terminal of a Van de Graaff accelerator, where it passes

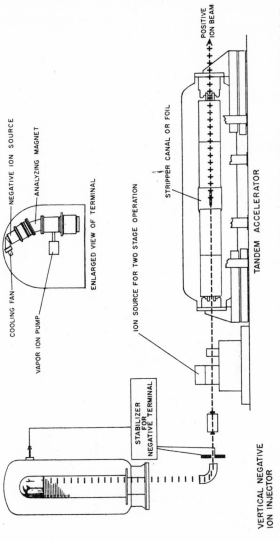

NEGATIVE ION SOURCE

ANALYZING MAGNET

COOLING FAN

VAPOR ION PUMP

ENLARGED VIEW OF TERMINAL

ION SOURCE FOR TWO STAGE OPERATION

STRIPPER CANAL OR FOIL

POSITIVE ION BEAM

TANDEM ACCELERATOR

STABILIZER FOR NEGATIVE TERMINAL

VERTICAL NEGATIVE ION INJECTOR

Fig. 3.5. Three-stage tandem with negative ion injection. (After P. H. Rose, 1961. *Nuclear Instruments and Methods* **11**, 49).

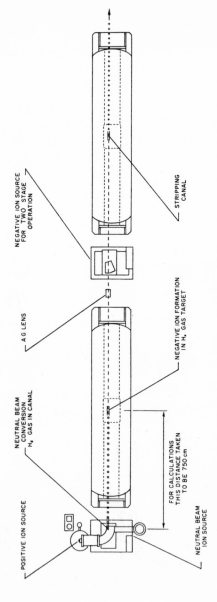

Fig. 3.6. Three-stage tandem with neutral beam injection. (After P. H. Rose, *op. cit.*).

through a second charge-exchange canal which converts some of the neutral atoms into negative ions by the attachment of another electron. These negative ions suffer their first stage of acceleration going to ground potential, where they are injected into a second machine operating at positive voltage. This is simply a two-stage tandem, where the already energetic negative ions are accelerated towards the positive terminal, pass through a stripper canal or foil, and once converted into positive ions drift to ground potential suffering the third and last stage of acceleration. If, as above, the voltage in each terminal is assumed to be 6 million volts, a three-stage tandem would yield 18-MeV protons and 60-MeV oxygen ions.

Alpha-particles are excluded from two- or three- stage acceleration since, as already mentioned, they do not form stable negative ions. Nevertheless, they can be made to drift as a neutral beam of helium atoms to the last stage of a tandem. They are stripped of electrons in the terminal and proceed thence to ground potential as in single-stage conventional accelerators.

5. The Cockcroft-Walton or Cascade Generator

The first nuclear reaction induced by artificially accelerated particles was obtained by Cockcroft and Walton in 1932. Important as their work was for nuclear physics, the technological achievement implied was no less significant. In fact, the generator named after them has been for many years a valuable tool for research not only in nuclear physics but in all those branches of science and engineering where high voltages are necessary. The effects of lightning upon insulators, for example, can be studied in the laboratory by producing one-million volts discharges with generators of this kind.

As in the Van de Graaff machine, high voltages are obtained in Cockcroft-Walton generators through the movement of electric charges. In the former they travel smoothly on the moving belt. In the latter their course is more uneven; they have to climb, as it were, a staircase. A sample 'step' of this staircase is enclosed in the dashed line of Fig. 3.7(a). The transformer T applies an a.c. voltage of maximum value V (typically 100 kilovolts) between two columns of condensers. These columns are marked A_0, A_1, A_2, A_3 and B_0, B_1, B_2, B_3 in the diagram. The point B_0 is connected to earth, so its potential will have a fixed value, say zero. The potential of A_0 oscillates instead between $-V$ and $+V$. The letters R_0,

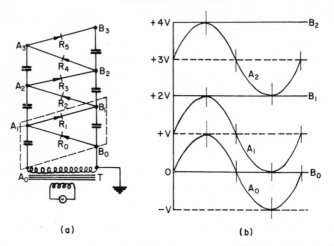

Fig. 3.7. Diagram of a Cockcroft-Walton generator: (*a*) Electric circuit. (*b*) Voltage in different parts of the circuit.

R_1, R_2, R_3 indicate rectifiers which only allow the passage of current in the sense shown by the arrow. That is to say, current will flow through R_0 whenever the potential of B_0 is greater than that of A_1. Assuming the condenser between A_0 and A_1 is initially uncharged, it will be left charged with the charge $Q = CV$ (C is the capacity) after the negative half-cycle. Once charged the condenser will maintain the potential difference V between A_1 and A_0 during the positive half-cycle, the point A_1 thus reaching the voltage 2 V with respect to earth. Part of the charge in A_1 will be therefore transferred through R_1 to the condenser between B_1 and B_0, and will be recovered by A_1 in the next negative half-cycle. After a few cycles B_1 will remain permanently charged at the maximum potential of A_1, that is, 2 V.

The next steps can be easily imagined. B_1 feeds the condenser $A_2 A_1$ through R_2 until A_2 acquires the same potential as B_1 during the negative half-cycle. In this way A_2 maintains a constant potential difference of 2 V with A_1, thus reaching the voltage 4 V in the positive half-cycle, at which B_2 remains permanently charged. Similarly a third stage would produce the potential 6 V at the corresponding point B_3, and so forth.

Summing up: the voltage oscillation at A_0 brings about a similar voltage oscillation in all the condensers in the left-hand column, in such a way that they can deliver part of their charge to the condensers in the right-hand column, during the positive half-cycle, being charged again during the negative half-cycle. If the number of stages is n, the voltage finally obtained is $2\ nV$. There is a constant voltage across any capacitor equal to $2\ V$. The only exception is $A_1 A_0$, whose voltage is only V, as can be seen in Fig. 3.7(b). For this reason it is usually made twice the capacity of the others, so that they may all hold the same charge.

We have not yet taken into account the possibility that the generator may deliver some electric current to the outside. Of course, if there were no such possibility, the generator would be useless. In practice such current is always drawn by the accelerated ions, corona effect, insulator leakage and a high-value resistor used as a voltage divider for measuring purposes. The steady current thus drained implies a steady discharge of the condensers, whereas the charge lost is replenished through the process described above only during a short interval per cycle. The voltage therefore drops steadily until the condensers are charged again. At this moment it increases suddenly, and the whole process repeats itself. The voltage therefore is not exactly constant, but oscillates between a maximum and a minimum value. This phenomenon, usually called 'ripple', is always present when a.c. voltage is converted into d.c. voltage, as in the present case.

A current drain also prevents the capacitors from becoming fully charged, and the generator delivers less than the nominal voltage in actual operation. We shall not tackle these problems extensively, but simply state the formulae corresponding to a generator where all the condensers have the same capacity C, with the exception of $A_1 A_0$, whose capacity is $2\ C$. If the generator has n stages, is operated at a frequency f, and delivers a current I, the voltage will oscillate between the values

$$V_{\max} = 2nV - \tfrac{2}{3}n^3 \frac{I}{fC} \qquad (3.6)$$

and

$$V_{\min} = V_{\max} - \tfrac{1}{2}n(n+1)\frac{I}{fC} \qquad (3.7)$$

because of the ripple effect.

The ultimate voltage cannot be increased indefinitely simply by increasing the number of stages. A maximum value is reached for

$$n = (VfC/I)^{\frac{1}{2}} , \tag{3.8}$$

which can be obtained by differentiation of eqn. (3.6).

The limitations of the Cockcroft-Walton machine are of a technological nature. There is a maximum voltage that the rectifiers, condensers and transformer can stand. Present-day selenium rectifiers set a practical limit for V around 100 kV, which is also typical of available transformers. According to formulae (3.6) and (3.7) it would be desirable to have as high a frequency as possible, but the losses in the transformer again set a useful limit of a few hundred cycles per second. Nevertheless, frequencies as high as 32 kc/s have been reported (Lorrain *et al.*, 1957) for a 500-kV generator.

Let us consider an actual machine. Typical values are:

$$V = 100 \text{ kV}$$
$$f = 200 \text{ c/s}$$
$$C = 0 \cdot 02 \text{ F}$$

Suppose we want to draw a maximum current of 4 mA. According to eqn. (3.8) the optimum number of stages is ten. From eqns. (3.6) and (3.7) we obtain

$$V_{\text{max}} = 1 \cdot 333 \text{ MV}$$
$$V_{\text{min}} = 1 \cdot 278 \text{ MV} .$$

Generators such as this are commercially available.

The ripple voltage is of course an extremely undesirable feature. It may be compensated to a certain extent using voltage regulators and filters, but it always produces fluctuations in the final energy of the accelerated particles. Nevertheless, Cockcroft-Walton machines are still widely used as sources of fast neutrons. Since neutrons, being uncharged, cannot be accelerated directly, they are produced by means of a nuclear reaction. In such a case, they may gain energy not only from the incident particle but from the intervening nuclear forces as well. A common example is the $D (d, n) He^3$ reaction, in which a deuteron hits another deuteron, capturing a proton to form He^3 and liberating a neutron. Most of the energy released in this reaction (3·26 MeV) is carried away by the neutron. In this way it is possible to obtain 4-MeV neutrons from 1-MeV incident

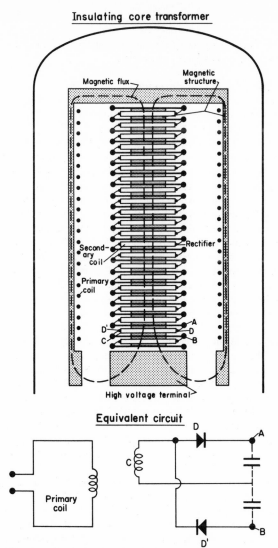

Fig. 3.8. Diagram of a single-phase insulating core transformer. (High Voltage Engineering Corporation, Burlington, Massachusetts).

deuterons. The effect of the ripple voltage upon the energy of the outgoing neutrons becomes relatively unimportant.

6. Insulating Core Transformers

Transformers are well-known electromagnetic devices. They consist of two coils, called primary and secondary. When an a.c. voltage is applied to the primary winding, the current flowing in it produces an alternating magnetic field. The field in turn induces an electromotive force on the secondary winding, whose value is $V_2 = (N_2/N_1) V_1$, where N_2 and N_1 are the number of turns in the secondary and primary coils, respectively, and V_1 is the a.c. voltage in the primary. In this way the primary voltage can be stepped up or down as desired according to the ratio of turns in both coils. The above relation is strictly valid only if the windings are such that the secondary links all the flux developed in the primary. This condition is usually met in practice by winding both coils around a common iron core. Although very efficient from the magnetic point of view, such transformers cannot deliver voltages in the million-volt range, being limited to a few hundred kilovolts. The limitation is due to the insulation required between the secondary (high-voltage) coil and the core, which is not far from ground potential.

In the insulating core transformer the iron core has not been dispensed with, but is made out of sections which are electrically insulated from one another. The segments form a central column surrounded by an outer shell of magnetic material, where the primary coil is wound. In this way the magnetic flux follows a path as shown in Fig. 3.8. Each section in the central core is surrounded by a secondary winding, where an a.c. voltage of about 30 kV is induced. The output from each secondary is rectified by means of the voltage doubling circuit shown in Fig. 3.8. The high voltage is obtained simply by connecting in series all the d.c. power supplies thus formed. This is most easily done through the distributed capacitance between core segments along the column.

In 1960 the first insulating core transformer was successfully operated at one million volts and 25 milliamperes, with a power conversion efficiency of about 90 per cent. It was the forerunner of more economical three-phase machines, now commercially available for the industrial irradiation of plastics. In such applications a single high-voltage generator may be used as power supply for several electron accelerators. This is just an example out of many industrial uses of accelerators.

7. Focussing

The discussion up to now has tacitly assumed that the particles moved on straight lines not far off the axis of the acceleration tube. But the ions are formed with random initial velocities, resulting in a divergent beam shortly after leaving the ion source. In the absence of external forces, the beam cross-section would tend to increase. The accelerating system should therefore provide such external forces as are necessary to constrict the beam along the axis. The art of attaining such constriction is called focussing. In the case of static accelerators it is achieved by properly shaping the electric field used in the acceleration. It has been mentioned before that the accelerating tube has alternate insulating and conducting sections, generally cylindrical. The potential drop is distributed along the whole structure through these electrodes. A field is therefore established between two of them whose lines of force and equipotential surfaces resemble those shown in Fig. 3.9. Referring to this figure, the acceleration

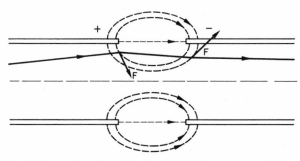

Fig. 3.9. Focussing effect of the electric field between two cylinders.

suffered by an off-axis particle coming from the left has components both along the axis and perpendicular to it. The latter is directed towards the axis in the first half of the gap between electrodes, away from it in the second half. In other words, the first half is focussing, the second defocussing. One may think at first sight that the whole radial effect averages out to zero, but this is not the case. In fact, since the particle gains energy while traversing the gap, it moves faster on the second half than on the first. The relative defocussing effect is smaller; the gap behaves with respect to particle trajectories exactly like a system of a convergent lens followed by a weaker divergent lens with respect to light rays. The result is a totally convergent system.

A succession of such lenses along the accelerating tube brings about the compression of the beam to a few millimetres in diameter, which represents a typical beam cross-section for scattering experiments.

CHAPTER 4

Linear Accelerators

1. The Concept of Resonance Acceleration

Linear accelerators have something in common with the machines described in the previous chapter: the acceleration is accomplished while the particles move on a straight line. But the accelerating electric field, instead of being due to a single high-voltage potential drop as in static accelerators, is produced by a high-frequency oscillating voltage, whose value is relatively small compared with the final energy of the particles. Repeated application of this voltage brings about the desired energy gain.

An alternating electric field changes sign periodically in time. When applied to a charged particle it will therefore be alternatingly accelerating and decelerating. An accelerator employing this sort of field must have some means of shielding the particles from the field during those half-periods when it is unfavourable for acceleration. This can be achieved by making use of the well-known fact that there is no electric field inside a hollow conductor, no matter what its potential as a whole may be. Early linear accelerators, whose basic principles are indicated in Fig. 4.1, had

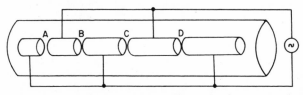

Fig. 4.1. Sketch of early linear accelerators. The accelerating gaps are shown as *A, B, C, D*.

cylindrical electrodes to which an alternating voltage was applied. The electric field was effectively restricted to the gaps between electrodes shown as *A, B, C, D* in Fig. 4.1. A particle could therefore be accelerated in each gap and drift inside the hollow cylinders during the unfavourable half-periods.

Since the particles have to spend the same interval of time (half a cycle of the oscillating voltage) inside each electrode, and their velocity increases as they gain energy, while the frequency is kept fixed, it follows that the length of the electrodes must increase accordingly. In other words, the length depends upon the particle velocity v through the equation

$$L = \tfrac{1}{2}v/f, \tag{4.1}$$

where f is the frequency of the applied electric field. The velocity, in turn, increases as the square root of the kinetic energy; if the applied voltage is V, the length of the n-th drift tube (as the electrodes are usually called) is

$$L_n = \frac{1}{2f} \sqrt{\left(\frac{2qVn}{m}\right)}, \tag{4.2}$$

where q is the charge of the particle and m its mass.

The first accelerator working along these lines (Wideröe, 1928) had three cylindrical electrodes. The alternating voltage was applied between the central electrode and the other two. Singly ionized atoms of sodium or potassium were injected into the machine; the field changed sign while they were drifting inside the central electrode, being favourable for acceleration at the crossing of both gaps. Three years later an accelerator having thirty drift tubes was reported (Sloan and Lawrence, 1931). It yielded 1·26-MeV mercury ions, with a peak voltage between electrodes of 42 kV.

In those machines, as well as in their modern descendants, the principle of *resonance acceleration* is at work. Although many particles (for example, those injected into the machine when the sign of the electric field is unfavourable for acceleration) are lost, some enter the machine at the proper phase of the electric field and keep in step with it until they reach the final energy. These particles are said to be in resonance with the accelerating electric field. As the reader will notice in the remainder of this book, all accelerators employing oscillating electric fields make use of this far-reaching principle, the ability to maintain resonance being their common feature.

The linear accelerators built during the thirties used radio-frequency fields of about 10 Mc/s, according to the oscillators then available. The machines were therefore restricted to the acceleration of heavy ions, since lighter particles, such as protons, would require much higher frequencies for drift tubes of reasonable length. This circumstance rendered their use in research rather dubious, so the interest in them was gradually lost. Radar developments during World War II provided at last the powerful oscillators (magnetrons, klystrons and special electron tubes) capable of producing radio frequencies of hundreds of megacycles per second, needed to accelerate protons and electrons successfully. Furthermore, another achievement, of conceptual rather than technological importance, was independently made in the U.S.S.R. (Veksler, 1944 and 1945) and in the U.S.A. (McMillan, 1945) by the end of the war; namely, the principle of phase stability, which applies not only to modern linear accelerators but to all high-energy machines as well.

2. The Principle of Phase Stability

The voltage applied between two successive electrodes of a linear accelerator can be expressed as

$$V = V_{\max} \sin \omega t , \tag{4.3}$$

if the time t is measured from the moment at which the voltage has zero value, and ω is the angular frequency of the electric oscillation. The *phase of a particle* can be defined as the value of the angle $\varphi = \omega t$ (taken to vary between 0 and 2π) at the time t at which the particle crosses an accelerating gap. In other words, the energy gain of a particle of charge q due to that particular crossing will be

$$\Delta W = qV_{\max} \sin \varphi . \tag{4.4}$$

It is clear that a particle in exact resonance with the electric field will have a constant phase during acceleration, corresponding to the energy gain for which the electrodes are designed.

In the early linear accelerators the length of the electrodes followed a law such as eqn. (4.2) with V replaced by $V_{\max}$. That is, for successful acceleration the particles had to cross the gaps when the electric field was near a maximum or, in more up-to-date language, their phase had to be close to $90°$. This arrangement, quite useful if just a few electrodes are required, becomes inefficient as the number of drift tubes, and consequently the energy, increase. For, consider in Fig. 4.2 a 'late' particle, arriving at a gap when the electric field has already passed its maximum value, and is already decreasing. Its energy gain being smaller than that of its more timely fellows, it will become slower than them and will be even later at the next crossing of a gap. The delay will become more important at each new crossing, until the particle will fall completely out of phase with the electric field, and will be lost for acceleration. An early particle, on the other hand, being also slower than it ought to be, will eventually reach the phase of 90°. But it will be already too slow by then; its phase will

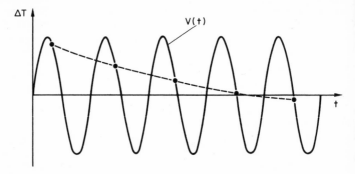

Fig. 4.2. Gradual loss of a 'late' particle in early designs of linear accelerators. The particle finally loses instead of gaining energy.

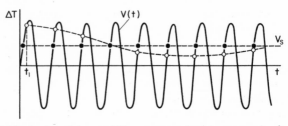

Fig. 4.3. Mechanism of phase stability. A non-synchronous particle (open circles) performs stable phase oscillations around the synchronous particle (full circles).

continue to increase and the particle will be transformed into a late one in the course of time.

If the system of drift tubes is built instead to match a voltage of, say, $V = \frac{1}{2}V_{max}(\sin \varphi = \frac{1}{2}, \varphi = 30°)$, the situation will be completely different, as shown in Fig. 4.3. We shall call *synchronous* those particles keeping exact resonance with the accelerating field, having therefore a constant phase $\varphi = \varphi_s$ ($\varphi_s = 30°$ in the example), and shall distinguish by a subscript s all parameters related to them. Referring to Fig. 4.3, a late particle, crossing a gap at time t_1 when $V > V_s$, will start moving faster than the synchronous particle. Its next arrival to a gap will not be so late as before, its energy will continue to increase above that of the synchronous particle, while its phase will approach the value φ_s. After a few crossings the phase may become equal to φ_s, but the particle will be already too fast and the phase will continue to decrease in subsequent crossings. But $\varphi < \varphi_s$ implies a smaller rate of energy gain than that of a synchronous particle, which will in turn compensate the higher energy of the particle. Our initially late particle will have become an early one, and the whole cycle will recommence again in the opposite sense. In short, particles somewhat out of resonance perform stable phase oscillations about the synchronous phase, undergoing the whole process of acceleration successfully.

In order to tackle phase oscillations more quantitatively we shall disregard the drift-tube structure of a proton linear accelerator, and consider the phase of a particle as a continuous variable. Taking the axis of the accelerator as z-axis, a particle of velocity v arrives at the point z at the time

$$t(z) = \int_0^z \frac{dz}{v}, \tag{4.5}$$

while the synchronous particle arrives at the same point at the time

$$t_s(z) = \int_0^z \frac{dz}{v_s}. \tag{4.6}$$

In terms of eqns. (4.5) and (4.6) the phase of an arbitrary particle may be defined as

$$\varphi = \omega(t - t_s) + \varphi_s, \tag{4.7}$$

while its rate of variation with time is

$$\dot{\varphi} = \dot{z} \frac{d\varphi}{dz} = \omega v \left(\frac{dt}{dz} - \frac{dt_s}{dz} \right) = \omega \left(1 - \frac{v}{v_s} \right). \tag{4.8}$$

We may, on the other hand, equate the rate of change of momentum with the force applied to the particle, obtaining

$$\dot{p} = qE \sin \varphi \tag{4.9}$$

and

$$\dot{p}_s = qE \sin \varphi_s \,, \tag{4.10}$$

where E is the electric field.

In order to combine together eqns. (4.8), (4.9) and (4.10), we shall make the simplifying assumption that the masses of the synchronous and non-synchronous particles do not differ appreciably. This is very approximately true for protons even in the semirelativistic region, extending up to about 100 MeV. Under this assumption (4.8) becomes

$$p_s \dot{\varphi} = \omega(p_s - p) \,, \tag{4.11}$$

which yields by differentiation, taking into account eqns. (4.9) and (4.10),

$$\frac{\mathrm{d}}{\mathrm{d}t} \left(p_s \frac{\mathrm{d}\varphi}{\mathrm{d}t} \right) + \omega q E(\sin \varphi - \sin \varphi_s) = 0 \tag{4.12}$$

We shall encounter a similar equation later, in connexion with the problem of phase stability in the synchrocyclotron (Chapter 6). Let us postpone its more complete treatment until then, and proceed now to study the particular case of small oscillations, where the difference between φ and φ_s is not too great. If such is the case,

$$\sin \varphi - \sin \varphi_s = 2 \sin \tfrac{1}{2}(\varphi - \varphi_s) \cos \tfrac{1}{2}(\varphi + \varphi_s) \simeq (\varphi - \varphi_s) \cos \varphi_s \,,$$

and (4.12) becomes the equation of simple harmonic motion, provided that the relatively slow variation of p_s is neglected. The resulting equation,

$$\frac{\mathrm{d}^2}{\mathrm{d}t^2} (\varphi - \varphi_s) + \omega_\varphi^2(\varphi - \varphi_s) = 0 \,, \tag{4.13}$$

where

$$\omega_\varphi = \left(\frac{qE \cos \varphi_s}{\omega p_s} \right)^{\frac{1}{2}} \omega \tag{4.14}$$

is the angular frequency of phase oscillations, admits an oscillatory solution only if ω_φ is real, which in turn implies that $\cos \varphi_s$ must be non-negative. This amounts to saying that φ_s must fall on the increasing slope of the electric oscillation, which was already implicit in our qualitative discussion above. More precisely, φ_s must lie between $0°$ and $90°$, since negative values would entail energy loss rather than energy gain. A synchronous phase of $0°$ corresponds to zero acceleration, whereas at $\varphi_s = 90°$ ($\omega_\varphi = 0$) the solution of (4.13) ceases to be oscillatory. At intermediate values of φ_s the solution is

$$\varphi - \varphi_s = (\varphi_0 - \varphi_s) \cos \omega_\varphi t , \qquad (4.15)$$

where φ_0 is the value of the phase at time $t = 0$. The equation (4.15) represents an oscillatory motion around the equilibrium phase φ_s. There is an associated oscillation of momentum around the value p_s, which can be obtained differentiating (4.15) with respect to time and replacing the result in (4.11); it is

$$p - p_s = \frac{\omega_\varphi}{\omega} p_s (\varphi_0 - \varphi_s) \sin \omega_\varphi t . \qquad (4.16)$$

The momentum (and energy) oscillation is therefore $90°$ out of phase with the phase oscillation. In principle the momentum oscillation might result in an undesirable lack of energy definition in the beam. Let us work out a numerical example to estimate this effect, considering 50 MeV protons in a linear accelerator working at a radio frequency of 200 Mc/s. A typical value for the electric field is 3 MV/m, and a synchronous phase $\varphi_s = 45°$ ($\cos \varphi_s = 0.7$) may be chosen. Since the kinetic energy T is proportional to p^2, the maximum relative energy error becomes, according to eqn. (4.16),

$$\frac{\Delta T}{T_s} \simeq 2 \frac{\Delta p}{p_s} = \pm 2(\varphi_0 - \varphi_s) \left(\frac{qE \cos \varphi_s}{\omega p_s} \right)^{\frac{1}{2}} . \qquad (4.17)$$

The numerical values given above yield

$$\frac{\Delta T}{T_s} = \pm 0.08 (\varphi_0 - \varphi_s) ,$$

that is, an energy spread of ± 2.1 per cent for an initial phase amplitude of $15°$. In practice, however, this is an overestimate: initial phase amplitudes are strongly damped as the acceleration proceeds (as a more exact treatment would have shown), resulting in a remarkably high-quality beam from the point of view of the energy spread, which can be as low as 0.5 per cent.

3. Proton and Heavy-Ion Linear Accelerators

The structure of modern linear accelerators differs markedly from that of their early ancestors. In these, the accelerating electrodes were fed directly with the oscillating voltage from an external generator. The electrode structure was aligned along the axis of an evacuated glass cylinder. This design becomes extremely wasteful of radio-frequency power in the range at which proton accelerators must be operated (about 200 Mc/s). In present-day machines the glass chamber has been replaced by a metallic resonating cavity, where a standing electromagnetic wave is generated, in much the same way as sound waves are generated in organ pipes. To this end, the output of an external vacuum-tube oscillator is fed into a large tank (usually made of highly conductive copper sheets), as shown in Fig. 4.4. The tank resonates at a sharply defined radio frequency,

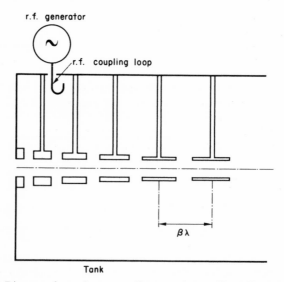

Fig. 4.4. Diagram of a modern proton linear accelerator. The drift tubes shield the particles from the electromagnetic wave during an entire period.

depending upon its shape and dimensions. A standing electromagnetic wave, reflected back and forth at the ends of the cavity, builds up inside. The electric field component of this wave is directed along the axis of the tank and provides the accelerating force acting on the protons. Since the acceleration process takes many periods of the radio-frequency field, drift tubes must be provided, as in the early machines, to shield the particles from the field during the negative half-cycles. But in this case the synchronous ions have to spend a full period inside the drift tubes to keep their phase constant. The distance between successive gaps is therefore,

$$L = \frac{v}{f} = \beta\lambda, \tag{4.18}$$

where $\beta = v/c$ is the ratio between the velocity of the particle and that of light, and $\lambda = c/f$ is the free-space wavelength of the accelerating field. The drift tubes are generally supported by thin stems attached to the walls of the resonating cavity. The cavity itself is usually contained in a larger vacuum steel tank, to avoid distortions under a change of pressure. Radio-frequency electric fields between 2 and 3 MV/m at 200 Mc/s are generally obtained with structures of this sort.

Cylindrical electrodes in a linear accelerator do not produce the same focussing effects as they do in the static machines described in the previous chapter. This is due to the oscillating nature of the field in the former type of accelerator. Let us recall that the field between two cylinders is radially focussing in the first half of the gap and radially defocussing in the second half. *If the field is constant in time*, the second effect is weaker than the first, because of the longer time that the particle spends in the first half of the gap. But this need no longer be true if the field changes with time. In the case of the linear accelerator, we have seen that all particles close to the synchronous phase (which form most of the useful beam) cross the accelerating gaps when the field is increasing with time. The field acting on the particle is therefore stronger in the second (defocussing) half of the gap than in the first. The rather unpleasant conclusion is that *phase stability is incompatible with radial focussing* in the linear accelerator.

The first of post-war linear accelerators was the 32-MeV Linac at the University of California. Electrostatic focussing was provided in this machine by distorting the electric-field pattern in the manner shown in Fig. 4.5 (b). To this end, very thin beryllium foils were located at the entrance of each electrode. The protons were pre-accelerated to 4 MeV in an electrostatic generator, so that they could traverse the foils without undue energy loss. But the foils were easily damaged by sparks that developed during radio-frequency build-up, and in the end the design had to be abandoned. Open grids were used instead, producing much the same field pattern as the foils, but at the cost of losing the particles hitting the tungsten strips that formed the grids (Fig. 4.5). Of course, high-energy injectors were not required any more; 500-keV Cockcroft-Walton generators are typical injectors for present-day linear accelerators. Such is the case, for example, with the Harwell 50-MeV and Minnessota 70-MeV machines. These accelerators also differ from the California Linac in the method by which focussing is achieved. Instead of using the machine's own electric field, additional magnetic fields are provided by means of magnets located inside the drift tubes. The precise operation of these magnetic lenses will be described in Chapter 7, when dealing with the principle of strong focussing. Their importance in connexion with the linear accelerator arises from the fact that grids can now be dispensed with and the beam intensity can consequently be increased.

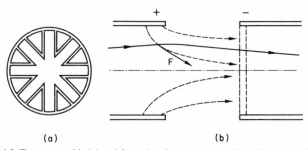

(a)   (b)

Fig. 4.5. Tungsten grids (*a*) and focussing force *F* produced by the electric field (*b*) in the 32 MeV Linac of the University of California.

The beam final energy in a linear accelerator cannot be varied smoothly, as is the case in the static accelerators described in the previous chapter. Nevertheless, a certain degree of flexibility can be obtained by constructing the accelerator in separated sections. The Harwell machine, for example, has three tanks. In the first the protons acquire a kinetic energy of 10 MeV, in the second they reach 30 MeV and leave the third at 50 MeV. If the third tank is not energized, 30-MeV protons are available at the output end of the machine. Similarly, the protons in the Minnesota accelerator attain 20 MeV in the first tank, 40 MeV in the second and 68 MeV in the third. Protons of all three energies can be used in different experiments.

The same principles can be applied to the acceleration of ions heavier than protons. Lower frequencies are required, 70 Mc/s being a typical value, and the corresponding increase in free-space wavelength brings about an increase in the dimensions of the resonating cavity. A proton accelerator operating at 200 Mc/s ($\lambda = 1 \cdot 5$ m) has a diameter of about 1 m, whereas the diameter of a heavy-ion machine ($\lambda = 4 \cdot 3$ m) may reach 3 m.

An interesting feature of heavy-ion accelerators is that they are not restricted to a single type of ion as proton machines are. In fact, successful acceleration will be attained as long as the ion velocity matches the drift tube length as suggested by eqn. (4.18). The velocity after traversal of the n-th gap can be expressed in turn as

$$v_s = (2nqV_{\max}\sin\varphi_s/m + v_0^2)^{\frac{1}{2}} \qquad (4.19)$$

where v_0 is the particle velocity at injection in the machine. Fortunately, most light nuclei have very similar values of the charge-to-mass ratio q/m. Taking the proton ratio as unit, $q/m = 0 \cdot 5$ for helium (two protons and two neutrons) and $q/m = 17/37 = 0 \cdot 46$ for the heaviest isotope of chlorine (17 protons and 20 neutrons). The first term under the square root in the right-hand side of eqn. (4.19) will maintain a constant value for different ions, provided that φ_s is suitably changed in each case. As a matter of fact, φ_s is implicitly *defined* by eqns. (4.18) and (4.19), so that the machine itself accommodates its synchronous phase to the electrode length according to the small changes in q/m for different ions.

A typical heavy-ion accelerator may have a 500-kV Cockcroft-Walton generator as an injector of doubly or triply ionized atoms. These particles enter the first stage of the accelerator, where they reach about a tenth of their final energy of about 10 MeV per nucleon. (As the reader may have noticed already, the machine fixes the final *velocity* of ions of any type; it is only natural that the kinetic energy be proportional to the mass of the ion, and therefore to the number of nucleons in it.) Before entering the next stage the ions are deprived of their remaining electrons, as in tandem Van de Graaff accelerators. They are subsequently accelerated to full energy according to (4.19).

A summary of the main features of some proton and heavy-ion linear accelerators is given in Table 4.1.

4. Electron Linear Accelerators

The electron mass is 1 836 times smaller than the proton mass. As already noted in Chapter 2, this fact implies that electrons will start being rela-

TABLE 4.1
Proton and Heavy Ion Linear Accelerators

Location	Particle	Injection energy (MeV)	Radio frequency (Mc/s)	R.F. power (kW)	R.F. pulse (μs)	Beam intensity (μA)	Length (m)	Energy (MeV)
Kharkov	p	1·7			250			21
Southern California	p	4	202·55	20	600	0·2	12·15	31·5
Moscow	p							40
Harwell	p	0·5	202	4 000	400			10, 30, 50
Argonne	p	0·75	200	2 500	500	5 000	33	50
Minnesotta	p	0·5	202·55	3 200	300	0·02	29·4	10, 40, 68
Kharkov	h.i.		150	500	500–3 000			9/nucl.
Manchester	h.i.	0·2	25	3 000	3 000		7·5	1/nucl.
Manchester	h.i.	1/nucl.	70–75	3 000	3 000		13·5	9–10/nucl.
Berkeley	h.i.	0·5	70	3 000	3 000	0·2	31·5	10/nucl.
Yale	h.i.	0·6	70	3 000	3 000	0·1	31·5	10/nucl.

tivistic (or, in other words, that their velocity will be close to that of light) at much lower energies than the protons. A 2-MeV electron, for example, has a total energy of 2·5 MeV, that is, five times its rest energy. Its velocity is the same as that of a 467-GeV proton, 0·98 c. Subsequent 'accelerations' do not result in an appreciable change in velocity but in an increase in mass.

If a drift tube structure were chosen for an electron machine, the electrode length would be, according to eqn. (4.18), roughly the same for all energies above 1 MeV ($\beta \simeq 1$) and equal to the free-space wavelength of the radio-frequency field. Such drift tubes might no longer be considered as small perturbations inside a large resonating cavity (their length would be greater than the diameter of the cavity), making the operation of such a system extremely uneconomical. It is possible to use a completely different approach, based upon the approximate equality between the electron velocity and that of propagation of an electromagnetic wave. Instead of generating a standing wave, reflected back and forth inside a closed cavity, a *travelling* wave is made to propagate along the axis of a metallic cylinder. Such a cylinder is called a *waveguide*. Electrons are injected into the guide and therafter are subjected to the longitudinal electric field component of the wave, which moves along with them. They suffer therefore a continuous acceleration and are driven by the wave in much the same way as foam is carried along by waves in the sea.

Phase stability is also at work in electron accelerators, although not exactly in the same way as in proton machines. In the present case the synchronous particle is fully fictitious, since it should move with the same velocity as the wave, that is, the velocity of light. This is an ultimate limit, which actual electron velocities will never reach. The phase oscillations and the associated velocity oscillations above and below the equilibrium values, appearing in proton linear accelerators, are no longer possible. Instead, a steady phase motion takes place inside the machine. Let us assume, for example, that the distribution of electric field E_z along the machine at a given instant is that shown as a full line in Fig. 4.6. A certain time Δt afterwards the distribution will look like the dashed line in that figure, the distance between two points of equal phase, such as A and A', being $\Delta z = c\Delta t$. Since the particles are slower than the wave, an electron initially at A will not reach the point A' after the time Δt, but a point such as A'', with a different phase. The phase will continue to change steadily, but at a slower rate as the electron velocity approaches the velocity of

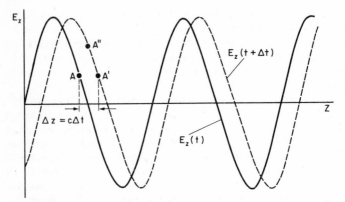

Fig. 4.6. Electric field patterns at different instants of time in an electron linear accelerator. Phase motion proceeds from A' to A'' towards an asymptotic phase.

light. In this way the phase will approach steadily a limiting value and the electron will become 'locked' to the accelerating wave.

A quantitative study of phase motion in this case makes use of the same equations (4.8) and (4.9) suitable for proton machines. The synchronous velocity is now constant ($v_s = c$), and eqn. (4.8) for the rate of change of the phase becomes

$$\dot{\varphi} = \omega(1-\beta) = \omega\left[1 - \frac{p}{(p^2 + m_0^2 c^2)^{\frac{1}{2}}}\right] \qquad (4.20)$$

where the last expression results from replacing the value of β as a function of momentum p. The rate of change of momentum is

$$\dot{p} = \dot{\varphi}\frac{\mathrm{d}p}{\mathrm{d}\varphi} = qE\sin\varphi . \qquad (4.21)$$

Replacing (4.20) into (4.21) a first-order differential equation is obtained, namely,

$$\frac{\omega}{qE}\left[1 - \frac{p}{(p^2 + m_0^2 c^2)^{\frac{1}{2}}}\right]\mathrm{d}p - \sin\varphi\,\mathrm{d}\varphi = 0 , \qquad (4.22)$$

which can be readily integrated to yield

$$\frac{\omega}{qE}\left[p - (p^2 + m_0^2 c^2)^{\frac{1}{2}}\right] + \cos\varphi = \text{const} = \frac{\omega}{qE}\left[p_i - (p_i^2 + m_0^2 c^2)^{\frac{1}{2}}\right] + \cos\varphi_i$$

(4.23)

where the subscript i refers to initial values of phase and momentum. As the electron momentum increases, becoming $p \gg m_0 c$, the first two terms on the left-hand side of eqn. (4.23) tend to cancel out. The phase approaches asymptotically a final value φ_f, which in terms of the initial total energy is

$$\cos\varphi_f = \cos\varphi_i + \frac{\omega W_i}{qcE}\left[\left(1 - \frac{m_0^2 c^4}{W_i^2}\right)^{\frac{1}{2}} - 1\right]$$

(4.24)

This equation is meaningful only if its right-hand side is smaller than one in absolute value. This amounts to a restriction on the possible range of initial phases acceptable for subsequent acceleration, which is quite broad in actual machines. Let us consider, for example, the 1-GeV electron linear accelerator at stanford University in the U.S.A. The electric field in this machine is 9·6 MV/m, oscillating at a frequency of 2 856 Mc/s. The electrons are injected into the accelerator with a kinetic energy of 80 keV, that is, with a total energy of 0·59 MeV. When these numerical values are replaced in eqn. (4.24) one obtains

$$\cos\varphi_f = \cos\varphi_i - 1\cdot 82 .$$

This restricts the range of initial phase to $0° < \varphi_i < 35°$, corresponding to $1 > \cos\varphi_i > 0\cdot 82$. The resulting asymptotic phases are in the range $145° < \varphi_f < 180°$.

The structure of electron linear accelerators differs markedly from the cylindrical-electrode pattern used for heavier particles. The waveguide is just a very long pipe, whose inside diameter is somewhat smaller than the free-space wavelength of the wave. In the above-mentioned Stanford machine the wavelength is 10·5 cm and the inside diameter is 8·247 cm. If the waveguide were completely hollow the phase velocity of the wave

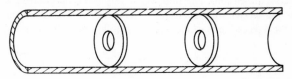

Fig. 4.7. Structure of the acceleration tube in an electron linear accelerator.

inside would not equal the free-space value c. For this reason, the tube contains equally spaced disks (irises) with holes in their centres to allow the passage of the beam, as shown in Fig. 4.7. The irises load the waveguide so that the wave is slowed down to the desired velocity. Alternatively, this structure can be regarded as a sequence of small resonating cavities, the opening in each iris serving the additional purpose of providing electromagnetic energy flow between one cavity and the next with such a phase shift that the resulting phase velocity matches the velocity of light.

The above is a sort of 'modular' design. Since the wave velocity is the same along the whole accelerator, the latter can be made out of identical sections assembled together. The basic unit is the resonating cavity limited by two irises. In the Stanford accelerator (Fig. 4.8) there are thirty sections, each one formed by five of those units. Each section is powered by a klystron amplifier, the total output being about 300 megawatts of radiofrequency power. In principle its energy like that of any other electron linear accelerator, could be increased indefinitely, simply by adding more sections. Indeed, this has been the case, since the machine has been in operation at 700 MeV for a few years, reaching the 1 000 MeV energy after the addition of eight new sections.

The requirement of constant wave velocity results in exacting demands on the construction of these accelerators. The different pieces have to be machined and installed with tolerances of a few microns, and the temperature along the machine must be kept under control during operation to prevent a change in the dimensions by thermal expansion.

A striking feature of electron linear accelerators is the absence of focussing lenses of any type. The same radial defocussing forces found in proton machines are at work, but, paradoxical as this statement may seem (the Stanford accelerator is 90 m long), machines are always too short to let them become effective. This is due to a relativistic effect, known as the Lorentz contraction, by which a moving observer sees all objects at rest shortened in the direction of his motion, but unchanged in their transversal dimensions. The 'observer' in this case is the electron, and the 'object' the accelerator. According to the theory of relativity, a length dz along the axis of the machine will be 'seen' by the electron as

$$dz' = \sqrt{(1 - \beta^2)}dz = \frac{W_0}{W}dz,$$

(4.25)

whereas its diameter will be the same as measured by a common observer

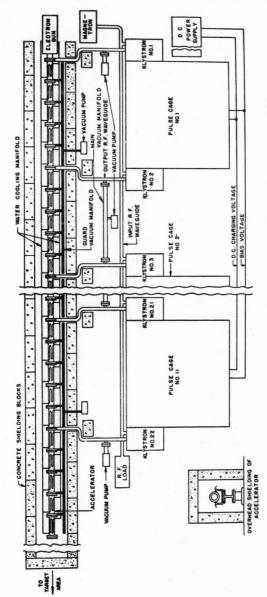

Fig. 4.8. Diagram of the Stanford linear accelerator. (From *Linear Accelerator Issue*, 1955).

in the laboratory. Let us now assume that the particles gain energy at a
constant rate along the accelerator, that is,

$$dW = \alpha \, dz \,, \tag{4.26}$$

or, according to (4.25),

$$dW = \frac{W}{W_0} \alpha \, dz' \,. \tag{4.27}$$

These two equations can be integrated to yield

$$W - W_0 = \alpha z \,,$$

$$W_0 \ln \frac{W}{W_0} = \alpha z' \,,$$

from which we obtain, by elimination of α,

$$z' = z \frac{W_0}{W - W_0} \ln \frac{W}{W_0} \,. \tag{4.28}$$

The last equation gives the actual length of the machine as seen by the
electron. The 180-m long, 2-GeV electron accelerator at Orsay, France,
becomes only 37·4 cm long, while the giant 45-GeV, 3 000 m machine
which has recently become operational at Stanford will not measure more
than 38 cm for the electrons inside.

5. Duty Cycle and Beam Structure in Linear Accelerators

It has been mentioned above that the radio-frequency power delivered
by the klystron amplifiers during acceleration in the Stanford machine is
300 megawatts. This is just as much power as is needed in a town of a few
hundred thousand people. Most of this power is transformed into heat,
and even if vacuum tubes existed capable of producing so much power
steadily, it would be a tremendous problem to remove the heat from the
accelerator. Instead, the oscillators are switched on and off sixty times a
second, providing as many bursts of accelerated electrons, which last one
microsecond each. The average power spent is obtained by multiplying
the power delivered during acceleration by the factor

$$\frac{\text{time the beam is on}}{\text{total time}} \,.$$

This is the machine's duty cycle. It measures how tightly the beam is
bunched in time.

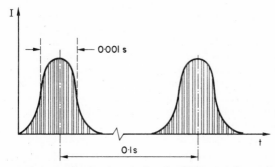

Fig. 4.9. Beam intensity distribution, as a function of time, in a linear accelerator. The shaded areas represent about 2×10^5 'sub-bursts', lasting 0·5 ns each.

Proton linear accelerators have duty cycles of about 1 per cent. Typical figures are 1 msec bursts ten times a second (Fig. 4.9). For quite different reasons, many other machines, with which we shall have occasion to deal below, have beams of a similar structure, with even lower duty cycles. This is an undesirable feature, at least from the point of view of the experimentalist who has to make use of these beams. In fact, the rate at which information can be obtained is in principle directly proportional to the intensity of the beam, since it determines the rate of production of the nuclear processes under observation. But even if the accelerator were able to supply a beam of unlimited intensity, the detectors and associated equipment set a limit to the admissible rate. They cannot register the production of a new event until they have finished processing the information from the previous one. This takes some time, which is called the 'dead time' of the instrument. Consider now a proton linear accelerator delivering a 1 μA beam (6.2×10^{12} protons per second). With a duty cycle of 1 per cent the counting equipment is busy only during the beam bursts, when the instantaneous current is 100 times larger. The equipment should be fast enough to handle a beam intensity of 100 μA, just to be idle 99 per cent of the time! In practice it is rather unusual to take advantage of the full beam intensity available, because of restrictions set by the counting equipment.

Power is needed to excite the resonating cavity simply because copper is not a perfect conductor. But some metals do become perfect conductors at temperatures just above the absolute zero, in their superconductive state. If it were possible to cool the whole machine down to such temperatures, it could be operated continuously with practically no power losses. The beam would be no longer pulsed, but continuous. Fantastic as this idea may seem, it has been seriously studied (Dickson, 1961 and Parkinson, 1962). The conclusions are that such a cryogenic accelerator would be feasible with present day techniques, although at an extremely high cost, particularly if account is taken of development work still needed.

In addition, the beam also possesses what could be called 'fine structure'. This is due to the damping of the phase oscillations in proton accelerators and to the restricted range of accepted initial phases in electron machines. In the first case the protons come out of the machine tightly bunched around the synchronous phase, forming a sort of 'sub-burst' in each radio-frequency cycle. The sub-bursts may last about $0·5$ ns (1 ns $= 1$ nanosecond $= 10^{-9}$ s), corresponding to 10 per cent of the radio-frequency cycle. The high frequency structure of the beam is used in certain experiments for the accurate measurement of very short time intervals. A typical example is the determination of the energy of neutrons produced in nuclear reactions by measuring their time of flight through a fixed distance. Neutrons are detected a few metres away from the target, and the time between their detection and the arrival of the next burst of protons is measured. Since the neutron is known to have been produced during one of the preceding bursts, its time of flight between target and detector, and therefore its energy, can be easily determined.

CHAPTER 5

Low-Energy Circular Accelerators

The accelerators considered so far achieve acceleration using only electric fields, which may be constant or variable in time. The electric field is in fact the only effective way of increasing the energy of charged particles. However, in what follows we shall have to deal with a new and important element, the magnetic field. We shall therefore recall some of the formulae already discussed in Chapter 2 which describe the effects of the magnetic field on electrons and ions.

A particle of charge q and velocity v moving in a plane perpendicular to the direction of a magnetic field B experiences a force

$$F = qvB . \tag{5.1}$$

In the case where the velocity has a component parallel to the magnetic field, the same formula applies with v standing for the normal component of the velocity, since the force is unaffected by the parallel component. This force, known as the Lorentz force, is normal both to the velocity and the field. Its effect is to bend the trajectory of the particle, whilst its kinetic energy remains unchanged. A particle moving on a curved path will be subjected to a centrifugal force which tends to re-establish rectilinear motion and whose magnitude will be equal to that of the Lorentz force:

$$qvB = mv^2/r , \tag{5.2}$$

where m is the mass of the particle and r the radius of curvature of the trajectory. If the magnetic field B and the energy are constant it follows that m, v and r will also be constant and the particle will perform uniform circular motion. Its angular velocity ω may be obtained from eqn. (5.2):

$$\omega = v/r = Bq/m . \tag{5.3}$$

We can also find a relation between the kinetic energy, the applied magnetic field and the radius of curvature of the trajectory:

$$T = \tfrac{1}{2}mv^2 = \tfrac{1}{2}q^2 B^2 r^2/m . \tag{5.4}$$

By means of these equations we can describe the first circular accelerator ever built: the cyclotron.

1. Principles of Operation of the Cyclotron

In 1930 Professor Lawrence, of the United States, and his collaborators were interested in the construction of a linear accelerator. We have seen the difficulties that the design of such a machine presented at that time. Lawrence realized that the succession of drift tubes could be replaced by only a pair of electrodes if the particles were compelled to cross the same accelerating gap repeatedly by means of a magnetic field (Lawrence and Edlefsen, 1930, Lawrence and Livingston, 1931, 1932). The result of this idea was an altogether different machine. The electrodes in the cyclotron are two hollow semicylinders, called 'dees' because of their shape, as seen in Fig. 5.1. Under the action of a magnetic field the ions will move along curved paths inside the dees, which are placed between the pole tips of an electromagnet. An a.c. voltage is applied between both dees, in such a way that the resulting electric field accelerates the ions whenever they cross the gap. Inside the dees the electric field is zero, so that if the particles are accelerated at one particular crossing, they will experience an electric force again only after half a turn, i.e., during the next crossing of the gap. If by that time the voltage has changed sign, the electric field will again favour acceleration, and the particles will gain energy steadily by a repetition of this process.

The ions originate in the ion source, located at the centre of the machine. Equation (5.4) shows that corresponding to their gain in energy by successive crossings of the gap between dees there will be an increase in radius. The resulting trajectory is therefore a spiral similar to the one shown in Fig. 5.1, although with very many more turns.

As indicated by formula (5.3), the angular velocity ω (angle swept in unit time) depends only on the magnetic field B and the ratio q/m between the ion's charge and mass. *If the mass remains constant* (which according to relativity is true when the velocity is small compared to that of light) and the magnetic field does not change, the angular velocity will be constant. But on the other hand we have already seen that to achieve successful accelerations the electric field should be in step with the motion of the particle, that is, its frequency is also constant and is given by:

$$f = \omega/2\,\pi\,.\tag{5.5}$$

This is the condition of synchronism between the particle and the accelerating field. As such, it is not only a requirement for acceleration but also a limitation on the maximum energies attainable with cyclotrons. In fact, the increase in energy brings about an increase in the mass of the ion and a corresponding change in the frequency of revolution. The ion will fall out of step with the electric field frequency and eqn. (5.5) will no longer be valid. The limit thus set is of about 15 MeV for protons, 25 MeV for deuterons and 50 MeV for alpha-particles. It would be absurd to use a cyclotron to accelerate electrons because their mass is already trebled at energies of about 1 MeV.

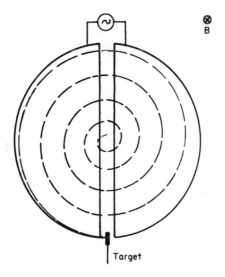

Fig. 5.1. Principle of operation of a cyclotron.

On the other hand, the magnetic field cannot be strictly uniform. If this were the case, a small component of velocity along the magnetic field would be sufficient to make the ion hit the pole face before the process of acceleration is over. Consider for example a deuteron with a speed of 10 km/s along the direction of the magnetic field immediately after leaving the ion source. This is not in fact too large a velocity: it corresponds to a kinetic energy of little more than one electron-volt, whilst voltages of hundreds of volts operate in the ion source. The deuteron may need about two hundred turns to reach the maximum radius. If the period of revolution is 10^{-7} s, which corresponds to a typical frequency of 10 Mc/s, the total time spent in the acceleration chamber will be 200×10^{-7} s $= 2 \times 10^{-5}$ s. In this time the initial velocity will produce a displacement of 10^6 cm/s $\times 2 \times 10^{-5}$ s $= 20$ cm. The distance between poles may be of about 30 cm, which means that the ion, having started from the median plane (equidistant from both pole tips), has had time enough to hit the magnet pole before reaching maximum energy. It is obviously desirable to have the particles confined to the neighbourhood of the median plane, an effect which is often referred to as vertical focussing. It is also necessary to have radial focussing, that is, if a particle moves away from its ideal circular orbit it should experience a force tending to restore it to the right position.

The problems of synchronism and focussing are basic in the design of any circular accelerator. The following paragraphs will be devoted to their study in connexion with the cyclotron.

2. Vertical Focussing in the Cyclotron
If the ions are to be kept in the vicinity of the median plane there must be forces returning them to this plane whenever they leave it. These forces may result from the particular shape of the magnetic field and that of the electric field in the accelerating gap. Magnetic focussing is by far the most important, and we shall describe it first.

The magnetic field in a circular magnet tends naturally to decrease near the edges of the pole tips, and the lines of force curve slightly outwards, as shown in Fig. 5.2. The field is still vertical in the median plane, but above and below it there are radial components of the field. The radial component, being normal to the velocity, will act upon the particle with a force of magnitude given by eqn. (5.1) and directed, as indicated in Fig. 5.2, towards the median plane. The situation is similar to that of a pendulum: a departure from the equilibrium position brings restoring forces into effect, the outcome of which are oscillations around the equilibrium position. In an entirely analogous way, the particles in a cyclotron suffer vertical oscillations above and below the median plane and radial oscillations around the equilibrium orbit. These are referred to as 'betatron oscillations', since they were first described (Kerst and Serber, 1941) in connexion with this machine.

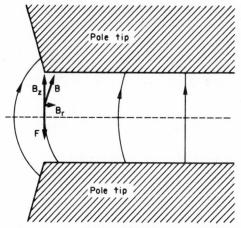

Fig. 5.2. Magnetic lines of force in a cyclotron. The focussing force F acting on a particle above the median plane results from the existence of a radial component of the magnetic field, B_r.

Let us describe the vertical oscillations in a more quantitative way. In order to do this, it is customary to relate the vertical component of the magnetic field B_{z0} at a radius r_0 with the same quantity B_z at a slightly different radius r by the equation

$$B_z/B_{z0} = (r/r_0)^{-n} , \qquad (5.6)$$

where the field index n is defined by:

$$n = -\frac{r}{B_z}\frac{dB_z}{dr} = -\frac{d \ln B_z}{d \ln r}. \qquad (5.7)$$

On the other hand, a static magnetic field in free space always fulfils the condition

$$\frac{dB_r}{dz} = \frac{dB_z}{dr} , \qquad (5.8)$$

where B_r is the radial component of the magnetic field shown in Fig. 5.2.

In the median plane the radial component $B_r = 0$ and at a short distance z from it the value of B_r can be obtained from eqn. (5.8) as:

$$B_r = \frac{\mathrm{d}B_r}{\mathrm{d}z}\,z \doteq \frac{\mathrm{d}B_z}{\mathrm{d}r}\,z = -(B_z nz/r)\,. \tag{5.9}$$

The vertical force F_z acting on a particle at a distance z from the median plane will then be

$$F_z = qvB_r = -qvB_z nz/r = -q\omega B_z nz = m\frac{\mathrm{d}^2 z}{\mathrm{d}t^2}\,. \tag{5.10}$$

Taking into account that $\omega = qB_z/m$, the equation for the vertical oscillations becomes

$$\frac{\mathrm{d}^2 z}{\mathrm{d}t^2} + n\omega^2 z = 0\,. \tag{5.11}$$

If n is positive this equation has the solution

$$z = A\,\sin\left[\sqrt{(n)}\omega t + \alpha\right] \tag{5.12}$$

where A and α are constants whose values are fixed by the initial conditions (for instance, the velocity of the deuteron when leaving the ion source in the example given before). The acceleration chamber must be made large enough to accommodate the amplitude A of these oscillations.

The condition that $n > 0$ implies, as seen from eqn. (5.7), that $\mathrm{d}B_z/\mathrm{d}r < 0$, that is, the magnetic field must decrease with radius if the vertical oscillations are to be bounded. This requirement prevents the adoption of a procedure which at first sight seems to remove the energy limitation of a cyclotron, namely, to increase the magnetic field keeping constant the ratio B/m and hence the frequency of revolution.

The electric field between dees not only accelerates the ions but may affect the vertical focussing. The lines of force are schematically shown in Fig. 5.3. (a); outside the median plane the electric field has a vertical component E_z which, assuming the particles come from the left, will first impel them towards the median plane (focussing) and then drive them away from it (defocussing). The net effect will be either focussing or defocussing depending upon the time of arrival of the particle at the gap.

This is due to the fact that the particle spends a finite time in a changing electric field when crossing the gap. The full line in Fig. 5.3 (b) is the

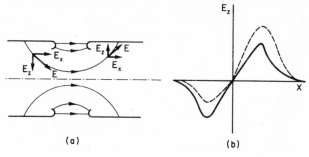

Fig. 5.3. Electric field between dees. (*a*) Shape of the lines of force. (*b*) Vertical component E_3 of the electric field felt by a very fast particle (full line) and by a slow particle arriving at the gap when the electric field increases with time (dashed line).

intensity of the vertical component as a function of position *at a given instant*; focussing and defocussing effects appear to be of the same magnitude and to compensate each other. But it takes some time for an ion to cross the gap: if the crossing is made *before* the voltage has reached its maximum value, that is, when the electric field is increasing with time, the particle meets a stronger field in the second (defocussing) half of the accelerating region than in the first. This is shown by the dashed line in Fig. 5.3(*b*). The defocussing field overcomes the focussing effect of the first half of the gap. Of course, the reverse is true when a particle arrives at the gap *after* the voltage has reached the maximum value: the over-all effect is then purely focussing.

We have again met the concept of phase of a particle with respect to the accelerating voltage. It is usual to define it by expressing the energy gain when crossing the gap as $qV_{max} \cos \varphi$, where V_{max} is the maximum voltage and φ is the phase. The phase is defined as positive when the voltage is decreasing with time, negative when it is increasing.

From our previous discussion it follows that it is desirable to have a positive phase, at least during the early stages of acceleration, where the magnetic focussing is relatively weak. Unfortunately, for reasons that will become apparent when studying synchronism, it is necessary to adopt a negative phase and consequently a certain degree of vertical defocussing due to the electric forces at the beginning of the acceleration. The cross-

section of the beam is shown in Fig. 5.4: the vertical height increases with
radius reaching a maximum at about half the final radius and then
decreases due to the vertical focussing provided by the magnetic forces.
The dees are shaped accordingly.

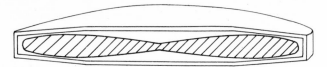

Fig. 5.4. Cross-section of the beam (shaded region) inside the dees, due to the
combined electric and magnetic focussing.

3. Radial Focussing

Radial focussing is achieved if a particle at a distance r from the centre,
different from the radius r_0 corresponding to its equilibrium orbit, is

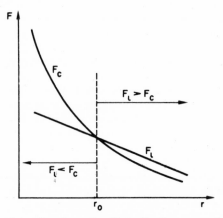

Fig. 5.5. Lorentz force, F_l, and centrifugal force F_c acting on a particle away from
the equilibrium radius r_0.

subjected to forces which tend to return it to the equilibrium orbit. Let us
assume, for instance, that $r > r_0$. Since the requirement for vertical
focussing is a decreasing field, the Lorentz force at radius r, qvB must be

weaker than qvB_0 at radius r_0. But also the centrifugal force, $mv^2/r*$, will have decreased, and provided the magnetic force does not decrease as rapidly as the centrifugal force, it will overcome the latter and tend to restore the particle to the original orbit. This is shown in Fig. 5.5, in which the magnitude of both forces is plotted as a function of r.

The presence of these forces results in radial oscillations similar to those we have found in the case of vertical focussing. We shall treat them assuming that $r - r_0$ is a small quantity. In such a case

$$r^{-n} \simeq r_0^{-n} - n r_0^{-n-1}(r - r_0),\qquad (5.13)$$

which, replaced in eqn. (5.6) above, results in the following approximate expression for B_z:

$$B = B_0\left(1 - n\frac{r - r_0}{r_0}\right).\qquad (5.14)$$

We have dropped the index z since we shall only be concerned with the field in the median plane, which has no radial component. The radial force produced by the magnetic field will then be

$$F_r = -qB_0\left(1 - n\frac{\rho}{r_0}\right)v,\qquad (5.15)$$

where $\rho = (r - r_0)$. The negative sign implies that the force is directed towards the centre. If the particle is moving away from the equilibrium orbit it will experience a radial acceleration $\mathrm{d}^2 r/\mathrm{d}t^2$ and a centripetal acceleration $-\omega^2 r = -v^2/r$. Newton's equation can then be written as:

$$m\left(\frac{\mathrm{d}^2 r}{\mathrm{d}t^2} - \frac{v^2}{r}\right) = -qB_0\left(1 - n\frac{\rho}{r_0}\right)v,\qquad (5.16)$$

or, after division by m

$$\ddot{\rho} - \frac{v^2}{r} = -\omega_0\left(1 - n\frac{\rho}{r_0}\right)v,\qquad (5.17)$$

where $\omega_0 = qB_0/m = v/r_0$ and the dots indicate differentiation with respect to time. We now take advantage of the smallness of ρ to write

---

* In this expression r is *not* the radius of curvature of the trajectory, as in (5.2) but the radius vector from the centre of the machine. They only coincide for the strictly circular equilibrium orbit.

$$\frac{1}{r} \simeq \frac{1}{r_0}\left(1 - \frac{\rho}{r_0}\right), \tag{5.18}$$

which transforms the equation into

$$\ddot{\rho} - \omega_0^2 r_0(1 - \rho/r_0) = -\omega_0^2 r_0(1 - n\rho/r_0)\,,$$

to yield, finally

$$\ddot{\rho} + \omega_0^2(1-n)\rho = 0 \tag{5.19}$$

Equation (5.19) is the equation for small radial oscillations. Just as in the case of vertical motion, its solution will correspond to bounded harmonic oscillations if $1-n$ is positive, that is, $n < 1$. This condition tells us again that the field must decrease more slowly than $1/r$, since, according to eqn. (5.6) it decreases as $1/r^n$.

Equations (5.11) and (5.19) also allow us to obtain the circular frequencies of vertical and radial oscillations. They are

$$\omega_z = \sqrt{(n)}\omega_0 \tag{5.20}$$

$$\omega_r = \sqrt{(1-n)}\omega_0 \tag{5.21}$$

respectively, with the condition that $0 < n < 1$. In a cyclotron n has the

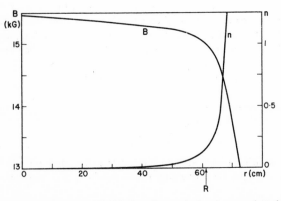

Fig. 5.6. Magnetic field B and field index n in a typical cyclotron, plotted against the radius. The values shown correspond to the machine described in paragraph 5, this chapter.

value zero at the centre, increasing gradually with radius (see Fig. 5.6). When it reaches the value 0·2 the ratio:

$$\frac{\omega_r}{\omega_z} = \left(\frac{1-n}{n}\right)^{\frac{1}{2}} = 2 \, .$$

The frequency of radial oscillations is an integral multiple of that of vertical oscillations. In this case there may be a transfer of energy between the two modes of oscillation, with the result that either the radial or vertical amplitude may increase beyond the limits in which the linear approximations we have used remain valid. This situation is known as a resonance, and it may imply the loss of the beam by the building up of the oscillations and the ions consequently hitting the walls of the acceleration chamber. This sets a new limit, namely $n < 0·2$, to the field gradient and the radius. The curves in Fig. 5.6 show the behaviour of the magnetic field and field index as functions of the radius in a typical cyclotron. The maximum useful radius corresponds generally to n values between 0·10 and 0·15, and is about 90 per cent of the pole radius.

4. Synchronism

We have seen how particles are automatically prevented from going too far away from the equilibrium orbit by means of radial and vertical focussing. The phase of an ion, which ultimately determines whether it will be accelerated or not when crossing the gap, does not enjoy stability. Moreover, we shall show that the particles tend to reach a phase which prevents their further acceleration after a certain number of turns. This fixes the maximum number of turns. Since the energy gain per turn depends on the voltage between dees, the final energy together with the number of turns determine the minimum voltage for successful acceleration.

There is a trend towards a lack of synchronism between the particle and the accelerating field because of the steady diminution of the angular velocity, due in turn to the decreasing magnetic field and the relativistic increase of mass with energy. If the frequency of revolution of a particle is smaller than that of the electric field, the latter will 'overtake' it, as shown in Fig. 5.7. A particle with phase $\varphi = 0$, crossing the gap at the moment of maximum voltage, will cross the gap again *after* the voltage has reached its maximum value. Its phase will become positive, according to our previous convention. This process will continue during subsequent turns until the phase will reach the value 90°, which implies no acceleration because the voltage is zero when the particle reaches the gap. In the next crossing the ion may meet a decelerating voltage, its circular frequency will increase a little and the phase will again be about 90°. There will be no further gain in energy, except for a succession of accelerations and decelerations corresponding to small oscillations of the phase around 90°.

The first few turns have a small radius of curvature, and the particles spend most of their period of revolution inside the accelerating gap. There is a very strong effect, due to the electric field, which results in a grouping of the particles around the phase $\varphi = 0$. This can then be considered the initial phase. If the electric frequency coincides with that of revolution near the centre of the machine, the phase will change as shown by curve I in Fig. 5.8 while the particle gains energy and radius. A simple example will show, however, that such a range of phases is extremely inconvenient. Let us consider a cyclotron to accelerate deuterons up to 20 MeV, in which the average magnetic field experienced by the ions is 1·5 per cent smaller than that at the centre, corresponding to a total decrease of

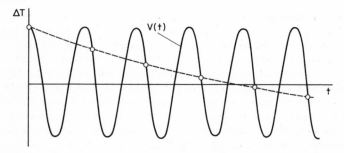

Fig. 5.7. Loss of synchronism due to the increasing period of revolution in a cyclotron. The energy gain per turn ΔT (open circles) is shown together with the electric oscillation as a function of time. Compare this situation with that of early linear accelerators, Fig. 4.2.

3 per cent; this is a fairly typical case. The mass increment at full energy is $20/1\,860 = 1·08$ per cent (the rest mass of the deuteron corresponds to 1 860 MeV), so we may take an average of 0·54 per cent. The average decrease in frequency of revolution can then be estimated as $1·5 + 0·54 = 2·04$ per cent and the phase shift in each turn will be $2·04 \times 360°/100 = 7·3°$;

since the total phase shift available is $90°$, the conclusion is that the whole process of acceleration must take place in $90°/7·3° = 12$ turns. With an average phase of $45°$ the peak voltage between dees must be: $V_{max} = 20\,000\ \text{kV}/(2 \times 12 \times \cos 45°) = 1\,180\ \text{kV}$. This number is just a crude estimate, and may be wrong by a factor of two; but even if radio-frequency

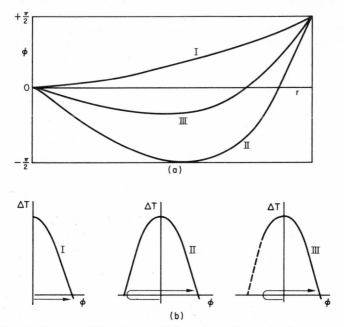

Fig. 5.8. Three possible variations of phase during the acceleration process. (*a*) Phase of the particles as a function of their radius. (*b*) Energy gain per turn depending on the phase. The arrows show the evolution of the phase in the three cases.

generators producing half this voltage were available, the problems of insulation inside the magnetic gap would be extremely complicated. There is an easier way of attaining the same energy with a smaller voltage: if the radiofrequency is smaller than the frequency of revolution near the centre of the machine (although greater than that corresponding to the maximum radius), the particles will overtake the electric field in the first few turns and the phase will become increasingly negative. It may even reach the value $-90°$, go back to zero, and finally to $+90°$, as shown by curve II of Fig. 5.8. This corresponds to the minimum possible voltage between dees. In such a case we can estimate that the number of turns is about three times greater than before, because there are $270°$ available for the phase shift compared to $90°$ in the previous case. The necessary voltage is proportionally reduced to about 400 kV. A more accurate analysis yields the curves appearing in Fig. 5.9, where the minimum voltage needed

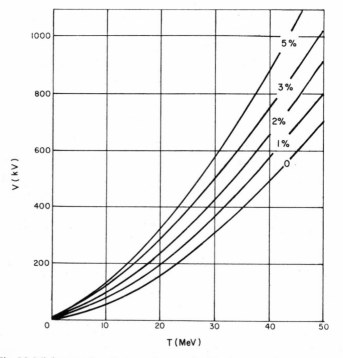

Fig. 5.9. Minimum voltage between dees required for the successful acceleration of protons. The final energy is plotted in abscissae. The curves correspond to different percentage variations of the magnetic field.

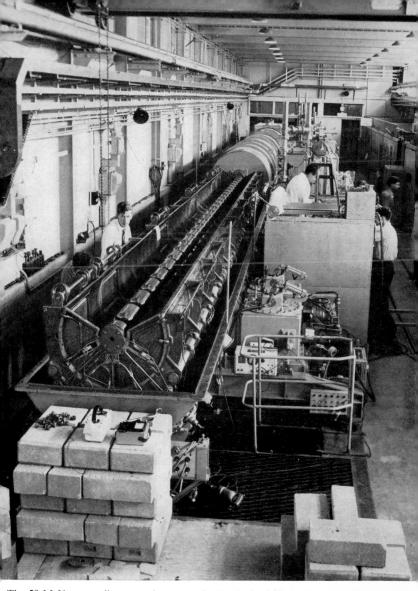

The 50-MeV proton linear accelerator at the Rutherford High Energy Laboratory, Harwell. The last tank, in the foreground, has the vacuum envelope and liner lids removed, showing the drift tubes. *(Courtesy of National Institute for Research in Nuclear Science)*.

2. An artist's view of Nimrod, the 7-GeV proton synchrotron at the Rutherford High Energy Laboratory, Harwell. The injector linear accelerator is shown at left, followed by the magnet ring where final acceleration takes

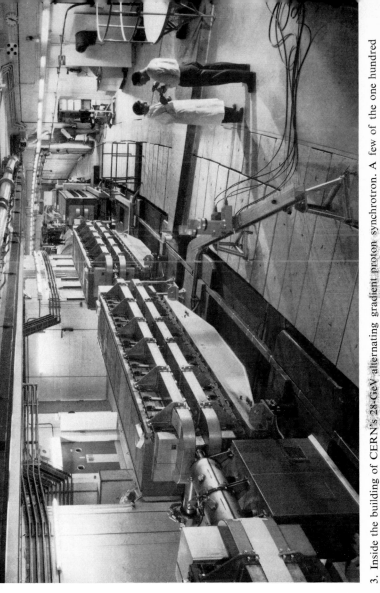

3. Inside the building of CERN's 28-GeV alternating gradient proton synchrotron. A few of the one hundred magnets providing the guiding field for the particles can be seen. (*Courtesy of CERN*).

4. Magnet of the 88″ azimuthally varying field cyclotron at the University of California. The walls of the square acceleration chamber have been removed. *(Courtesy of Lawrence Radiation Laboratory)*.

is plotted against the final energy attainable for different values of the total magnetic field variation.

It has been mentioned before that a negative phase brings about a vertical defocussing by the electric field. This effect is particularly important at low energies, near the centre of the machine. For this reason a higher voltage than the minimum is generally used and the phase follows a curve like III in Fig. 5.8, with a maximum negative value of $-30°$.

5. Design Features of Cyclotrons

We can now determine the main parameters in the design of a cyclotron. Let us consider two cyclotrons of the same energy, 20 MeV, one for protons and the other for deuterons. We start by working out the magnet radius. In fact the magnet is generally the most costly piece of equipment, its cost being approximately proportional to the cube of the linear dimensions. The size is reduced as much as possible by choosing a strong field, of the order of 15 000 gauss ($1·5$ weber/m^2). The radius is obtained from eqn. (5.4):

$$R = (2\ Tm)^{\frac{1}{2}}/qB = (2\ Vm/q)^{\frac{1}{2}}/B$$

where V now stands for the energy in eV. Replacement of the numerical values from Table 1.1 with $B = 1·5$ weber/m^2 yields:

$$R = 0·43 \text{ m} \quad \text{for} \quad 20 \text{ MeV protons ;}$$
$$R = 0·61 \text{ m} \quad \text{for} \quad 20 \text{ MeV deuterons .}$$

This is the radius at full energy. The pole radius will be about 10 per cent larger.

We shall choose a relative decrease of 3 per cent for the magnetic field. With this requirement the field at the centre must be 15 450 gauss. On the other hand, the ions will suffer a fractional increase in mass given by $T/m_0 c^2$, that is $2·14$ per cent for protons and $1·08$ per cent for deuterons. The proton and deuteron masses, originally $1·670 \times 10^{-27}$ kg and $3·340 \times 10^{-27}$ kg respectively, will be $1·706 \times 10^{-27}$ kg and $3·376 \times 10^{-27}$ kg at full energy. The frequencies of revolution can be obtained from the expression $f = qB/2\pi m$; their values at radii $r = 0$ and $r = R$ are:

$$f_0 = 23·6 \text{ Mc/s} \quad \text{and} \quad f_R = 22·4 \text{ Mc/s} \quad \text{for protons, and}$$
$$f_0 = 11·8 \text{ Mc/s} \quad \text{and} \quad f_R = 11·3 \text{ Mc/s} \quad \text{for deuterons .}$$

The value of the electric frequency falls between those of f_0 and f_R. More precisely, it must be equal to the frequency of revolution of a particle with the minimum (negative) phase, and this generally corresponds to a radius at which the particle has attained about one third of the full energy.

Finally, we have to determine the peak voltage between dees. Its minimum value can be obtained from the curves of Fig. 5.9, which in our case (3 per cent decrease in B) is 300 kV for 20 MeV protons. Deuterons would require approximately half this value. These voltages will produce phase curves like II in Fig. 5.8. In practice higher voltages are needed to obtain curve III, of about 400 kV for protons and 200 kV for deuterons. The voltages required pose extremely difficult problems of insulation in the restricted space available inside the acceleration chamber. In most machines one dee is negative while the other is positive, so the potential difference between any dee and the chamber is only half that between both dees. The insulation required is therefore also halved. Even with this arrangement, the construction of a cyclotron to accelerate protons up to 20 MeV has never been attempted, although quite a few exist in the United States and Europe producing deuterons of that energy.

On the other hand, a cyclotron for deuterons has the advantage of its versatility: the machine we have been studying would also accelerate alpha particles up to 40 MeV and protons up to 10 MeV. In fact, the alpha-particles have twice the charge and twice the mass of the deuterons, and consequently the same ratio q/m; their frequency of revolution, according to eqn. (5.3), will be the same as that of the deuterons, and all the conditions for synchronism will be fulfilled with the same magnetic field and radio frequency. But the value of q^2/m is twice that of deuterons, yielding twice the kinetic energy in eqn. (5.4). As for protons, they have the same charge and half the mass of the deuterons. It suffices to reduce the magnetic field by a factor of two to obtain the same frequency of revolution but half the final energy. An alternative procedure is to accelerate, instead of single protons, ionized hydrogen molecules; this system of two protons and one electron will simulate a deuteron, and the final energy (20 MeV in our case) will be shared by both protons. By suitably adjusting the magnetic field in the form outlined above these machines have been used in recent years to accelerate He^3 nuclei (to two thirds the deuteron energy), heavy ions, etc. For this reason the cyclotron in our example would be generally referred to as producing 10 MeV per nucleon. It is also understandable why the great majority of the existing cyclotrons are actually deuteron machines.

6. The Betatron

A magnetic field can also be used for the acceleration of electrons in circular orbits in a machine called a betatron. Its characteristic feature is the absence of electrodes of any kind to produce the electric field which, as already mentioned, is the only effective agent in the acceleration of charged particles. The electric field arises instead from the *variation in time* of the magnetic field. We have studied this phenomenon in Chapter 2: the variation of magnetic flux across a surface induces a voltage along the closed curve bounding this surface given by

$$V = - \frac{d\Phi}{dt} \tag{5.22}$$

where Φ is the magnetic flux and $d\Phi/dt$ its rate of change with time. Consider now the electrons travelling in circular orbits under the action of a magnetic field. If the field varies in time (for instance, increases) the flux embraced by the orbit will also change inducing a voltage and consequently an electric field E along the orbit given by:

$$E = - \frac{V}{2\pi r} = \frac{1}{2\pi r} \frac{d\Phi}{dt} = \frac{r}{2} \frac{d\bar{B}}{dt}. \tag{5.23}$$

The last expression is obtained by replacing Φ by its value $\pi r^2 \bar{B}$, where $\bar{B}$ is the average magnetic field inside the orbit. The reason for keeping the orbit radius r fixed while carrying out the differentiation will be seen presently. The electric field will have either sign according to whether the flux increases or decreases in time. The electric forces will bring about a gain in the electron energy and the orbit will correspondingly tend to expand. An expansion of the orbit is inevitable if the magnetic field decreases in time, but it is conceivable that an *increase* of the magnetic field could compensate the tendency towards an increasing radius and result in a stationary orbit for the whole process of acceleration. This is precisely the basic principle in the betatron.

The field must of course fulfil certain conditions if the orbit is to remain fixed. They are easily obtained with the aid of the equations at the beginning of this chapter. We start by noting that eqn. (5.2) implies that the linear momentum depends on the magnetic field and the orbit radius:

$$mv = qBr. \tag{5.24}$$

Let us now assume that the radius r is constant: a change in the magnetic field dB requires a corresponding variation in momentum

$$d(mv) = qr dB .$$

The laws of mechanics on the other hand establish that the variation of momentum during a short time interval must be equal to the applied force (in our case qE) times the time of application:

$$d(mv) = qE\,dt = q\,\frac{r}{2}\,\frac{d\bar{B}}{dt}\,dt = q\,\frac{r}{2}\,d\bar{B} .$$

Both expressions for the variation of momentum can now be equated, yielding

$$d\bar{B} = 2\,dB ,$$

or, after integration:

$$\bar{B} = 2\,B . \tag{5.25}$$

This is the fundamental condition for acceleration in a stable orbit: the average magnetic field *inside* must be twice the field *on* the orbit. Neither the mass nor the velocity of the particles appear in this relation. Its fulfilment allows the acceleration of electrons practically from rest to velocities close to that of light, always on the same orbit, provided the magnet has been suitably constructed.

From the condition (5.25) it follows that the field near the centre must be much higher than on the orbit. The field is strongly decreasing, thus providing good vertical and radial focussing, with n values around 0.7. Since the electrons remain always on the same orbit, the acceleration chamber is shaped like a torus. For this reason it is usually called a 'doughnut'. The crosssection is shown in Fig. 5.10. The pole pieces are closer together near the centre to provide the high flux needed in that region.

It is obvious that the process of acceleration cannot be continuous, for the simple reason that the magnetic field cannot increase indefinitely. The magnet coils are excited with alternating current, as shown in Fig. 5.11, the intervals of decreasing field being useless for acceleration. Moreover, as the sign of the magnetic field must be constant during the acceleration, it is usual to apply a fixed field besides the alternating (accelerating) field such that the total field never changes sign (see Fig. 5.11). The period of acceleration is thus doubled.

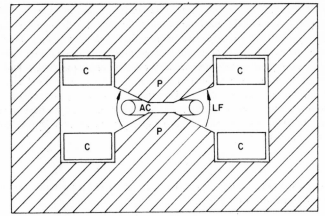

Fig. 5.10. Structure of a betatron. Pole pieces (P), acceleration chamber (AC), coils (C) and lines of force (LF) are shown.

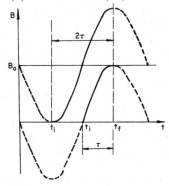

Fig. 5.11. Variation of the magnetic field of a betatron with time. The period of acceleration (full line) is doubled when a suitable constant field is added to the alternating field.

7. Design Parameters of a Betatron

We can, as we did with cyclotrons, work out the main parameters of a typical betatron. Let us take an energy of 20 MeV for the sake of comparison with the cyclotron calculations: it is exactly the energy chosen by

Kerst, inventor of the betatron, to design his second machine in 1942.
First we have to fix the maximum value of the magnetic field on the orbit.
Since the field at the centre must be more than twice that on the orbit, the
requirement that the iron should saturate nowhere rules out very strong
fields; 4 000 gauss is a suitable value. We cannot apply the same equation
for the orbit radius used in the cyclotron case because the final kinetic
energy will now be about *forty times* that corresponding to the electron
rest mass. The classical formulae are no longer valid and we have to use
the relativistic ones instead. In such a case the total energy W is related
to the momentum by:

$$W^2 = (m_0 c^2)^2 + (mv)^2 c^2 ,$$

where, as usual, c is the velocity of light and m_0 the rest mass of the electron.
The momentum is then:

$$mv = [W^2 - (m_0 c^2)^2]^{\frac{1}{2}}/c . \tag{5.26}$$

The electron rest energy is 0·51 MeV; its total energy after acceleration
will then be 20·51 MeV. Replacing the numerical values one finds
$r = 0·172$ m, much smaller than the radius of a cyclotron of similar energy.

The frequency of the oscillating magnetic field still remains to be fixed.
It would seem that since the energy depends only on the final (maximum)
value of the magnetic field it should be unimportant whether this value is
reached in a long or a short time, but the current of accelerated electrons
is proportional to the number of acceleration cycles per second, thus
making it desirable to have as large a frequency as possible. The limit is
actually set by the losses resulting from eddy currents in the magnet iron.
A typical value is 50 c/s. This means that the electrons reach their maximum
energy in about a hundredth of a second; if the electrons move with the
velocity of light (which is practically true for energies above 2 MeV) they
will have travelled 3 000 km on their orbit, or 2·8 million turns, in one
acceleration cycle.

It would be wrong to assume that a sufficiently large betatron would
provide electrons accelerated up to any desired energy. On the contrary,
there are limitations on the maximum energy attainable, although of a
completely different nature from those existing in the cyclotron. The
limitations arise from the fact that according to the laws of electrodynamics, a charged particle suffering an acceleration will emit electro-

magnetic radiation. Since a particle revolving in a closed orbit must be necessarily subjected to a centripetal acceleration, it will lose some energy in the form of radiation in every turn. This effect becomes more important when the particle velocity is close to that of light; for this reason we do not need to concern ourselves with it when dealing with cyclotrons, in which the particles would rarely have a velocity exceeding $0.14 c$. But the high velocity electrons in a betatron are an altogether different matter: at about 400 MeV they would yield as radiation the few electron-volts (7 eV in our 20-MeV betatron) they gain in each turn, thus making any further acceleration impossible. In some machines the radiation falls within the visible spectrum, and the electrons can be 'seen' through the light they emit.

Instead of an ion source, the betatrons have what is called an 'electron gun'. The electrons originate in a heated filament and are accelerated by voltages ranging from a few hundred to a few thousand volts according to the particular machine. It is obvious that the electron gun cannot be placed on the acceleration orbit, since in such a case the electrons would hit its back at the end of their first turn. It is therefore located outside the orbit. The electrons are injected along a path similar to that shown in Fig. 5.12 by a voltage pulse in the electron gun, properly timed to coincide with the starting of the acceleration cycle. With a field index $n = 0.75$, the frequencies of betatron oscillations are $f_r = 0.5 f_0$ and $f_z = 0.86 f_0$ (cf. eqns. (5.20) and (5.21)). In the first turn after injection the electrons will be in the minimum of their radial oscillation and will therefore miss the electron gun. They will reach the radial maximum in the second turn, but a certain fraction will still miss the injector because their vertical motion will be near its maximum by then. This mechanism, together with the progressive damping of the oscillations, may contribute to at least part of the beam intensities observed. Other effects, such as selfcontraction of the orbit (Kerst, 1948), are also likely to play a role in the process.

8. The Microtron or Electron Cyclotron

This machine, invented during World War II (Veksler, 1944), serves, like the betatron, for the acceleration of electrons. It has the advantage of a continuous beam, whereas betatrons have duty cycles of the order of 10^{-4}. On the other hand, the energies attained with microtrons are in the range of 10 to 20 MeV, much lower than those achieved with betatrons.

The principles of operation are sketched in Fig. 5.13. A short electron

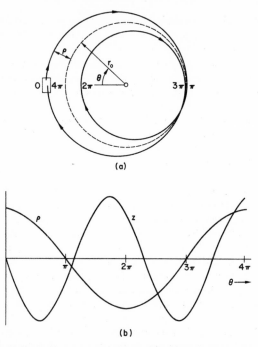

(a)

(b)

Fig. 5.12. (a) Initial orbits in a betatron with $n = 0.75$. (b) Dependence of the radial and vertical oscillations with azimuthal angle.

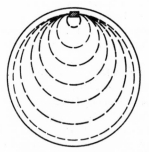

Fig. 5.13. Electron trajectories in a microtron.

linear accelerator comprising a single resonating cavity yields energy gains of 0·51 MeV. This is exactly the electron rest energy, so electrons starting from rest will leave the cavity with twice their initial mass. The cavity is located between the pole tips of a magnet producing a homogeneous magnetic field, as shown in Fig. 5.13. The electrons will describe a circular orbit in the field, with a period of revolution.

$$\tau_1 = 2\pi/\omega_1 = 4\pi m_0/(qB) = 2\tau_0, \qquad (5.28)$$

where τ_0 is the period of revolution corresponding to the rest mass of the electron in the same field. Once having performed the first revolution the electrons re-enter the cavity, to be accelerated again. This second acceleration will be successful if the period of oscillation of the electric field is exactly τ_0. In such a case their phase in the second acceleration will be the same as in the first. They will leave the cavity with a mass $m_2 = 3m_0$ and will perform a revolution in the magnetic field with period $\tau_2 = 3\tau_0$, after which they will come again into the cavity. A similar mechanism operates in successive revolutions.

The requirement of a homogeneous magnetic field throughout the machine prevents the achievement of good vertical focussing, as would be the case if the field decreased with radius. This in turn limits the number of revolutions to be performed without undue loss of the beam and therefore the maximum energy attainable.

Only a few electron cyclotrons are in operation. An excellent description of one of them as well as of the underlying theory will be found elsewhere (Henderson *et al.*, 1953).

9. Beam Extraction from Circular Machines

Experiments of the type sketched in Fig. 1.1 cannot be carried out in the limited space available inside an acceleration chamber. The particles must be extracted out of the machine and made to follow straight paths until they hit the target located in a separate chamber.

In the cyclotron, every increase in the particle energy is associated with an increase in the radius of the equilibrium orbit. Differentiating eqn. (5.4) one finds

$$\Delta r/r = \tfrac{1}{2}\Delta T/T. \qquad (5.29)$$

It is out of the question to let the particles spiral out of the magnetic field by themselves. The beam would be destroyed when reaching the radius of $n = 0.2$ (cf. the end of Section 3), which is still well inside the field. Instead, the beam may be deflected out of its circular path by the electric field created between two metallic plates, as shown in Fig. 5.14. This will be possible if the separation between two successive orbits is sufficiently large so that the particles can skip the inner plate when entering the channel formed by both plates. According to eqn. (5.29) the orbit separation depends on the energy gain per turn. Consequently the radius for extrac-

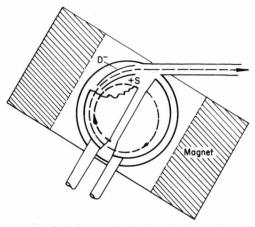

Fig. 5.14. Beam extraction in a conventional cyclotron. D, deflector. S, septum.

tion must be chosen such that curve III of Fig. 5.8 yields a phase not too close to 90°, where the energy gain is zero. A final phase of 60° (cos $\varphi = 0.5$) is typical. In the example given above of a 20-MeV deuteron cyclotron with 200 kV between dees, the energy gain in the last turn would be 200 keV. If this value is replaced in eqn. (5.29), together with $T = 20$ MeV and $r = 61$ cm, an orbit separation of 3 mm is obtained. It is therefore possible to interpose a thin tungsten or molybdenum foil between both orbits. This foil is called a 'septum' and is electrically connected to the dee inside which the deflector is mounted. The outer plate is connected to a negative high voltage supply. In this way a field of about 80 kV/cm is formed, extending about 90°, which brings the outgoing particles far enough from the circulating beam. They are then injected into an iron pipe, where the magnetic field is greatly reduced, to be finally conveyed out of the machine.

In betatrons a pulsed magnetic field of short duration produced by an auxiliary coil, is applied at the end of each acceleration cycle. This field induces radial oscillations in the beam, making it hit a target located inside the acceleration chamber but outside the normal orbit. This is the usual procedure when the x-rays produced in the target are wanted, but not the electron beam itself. If this is not the case the oscillations are made of large enough amplitude for the beam to be directed into a magnetic channel where the magnetic field is small, allowing the electrons to follow an almost straight path out of the machine.

CHAPTER 6

High-Energy Circular Accelerators

The accelerators we have studied so far suffer from limitations to their maximum energy. These limitations are actually only relative, in the sense that they are brought about by technological and financial considerations rather than by the principles of operation of the machines themselves. A conventional cyclotron of the type described in the previous chapter, for example, can yield particles of any desired energy provided that extremely high voltages are applied to the dees to produce the acceleration in a few hundred turns. And, in fact, what is now the California synchrocyclotron, accelerating protons up to 750 MeV, was originally designed as a huge conventional cyclotron although only the original magnet was used for the present machine. Similarly, there is no limit to the energy attainable with a linear accelerator if it is made long enough. The point is that the cost of these machines becomes forbiddingly high as they are made larger and larger. The difficulty has been circumvented as new concepts made their appearance. The acceleration of nuclear particles to relativistic energies was only made possible by the advent of the principle of phase stability, which we have already encountered when dealing with the linear accelerator. When applied in conjunction with a magnetic guiding field, this principle has resulted in accelerators whose cost per MeV (although not necessarily the total cost) is even lower than that of smaller machines.

In the case of the cyclotron, we have already seen that the lack of phase stability, or rather, the fact that the only stable phase is that for which there is no acceleration, brings about a strong limitation on the energy attainable. If one could shift this stable phase to such a value that the corresponding energy gain per turn were different from zero, there would be no limit to the final energy. This is, indeed, the characteristic feature of the accelerators that we shall study in this chapter. According to the way in which this phase stability is achieved, we shall have to study the synchrocyclotron, the proton synchrotron and the electron synchrotron. All these machines are also generically called synchrotrons.

1. The Synchrocyclotron or Frequency-Modulated Cyclotron

The synchrocyclotron may be described as a conventional cyclotron in which the frequency of the oscillating voltage applied to the dees changes periodically with time. In a cyclotron, the frequency of revolution of the ions,

$$f = \frac{\omega}{2\pi} = \frac{qB}{2\pi m},$$

decreases as their energy increases. First, because of the relativistic increase of mass with energy (if T is the kinetic energy, and m_0 the rest mass of a particle, the total energy $W = T + m_0 c^2 = mc^2$; see Chapter 2). Second, because the magnetic field must decrease with radius to provide vertical focussing for the beam. If the radio frequency is kept constant a lack of synchronism between the particles and the alternating voltage must necessarily follow which puts an end to the process of acceleration. But if the radio frequency decreases with time, matching the motion of the particles, it may be expected that they will not fall out of step with the electric field.

It is relatively easy to produce a *total* variation of the radio frequency equal to the change in the frequency of revolution, in more or less the same time that the particle takes to travel from the ion source in the centre of the machine to the radius of maximum energy. But it is impossible that both frequencies be the same at *any* time, not only because of the complicated laws of variation of the field and the mass, but also because each individual particle has its own history, depending upon the time of ejection from the ion source, collisions with molecules of residual gas, etc. All the same, although the coincidence may not be complete, the mechanism of phase stability catches the particles and guides them through the process of acceleration. This is shown schematically in Fig. 6.1.

In order to study how phase stability operates in a synchrocyclotron we shall have to define an ideal particle whose frequency of revolution is the same as that of the accelerating voltage at every instant of time. The actual existence of such particles is of little importance for our analysis. The synchronous particle, as it is called, manages to cross the accelerating gap at times at which the voltage has a certain value which is always the same. Its energy gain per turn is therefore fixed. Since the frequency varies with time, we express the alternating voltage between dees as $V_{max} \sin\left[\int_0^t \omega_s(t) dt\right]$, where $\omega_s(t)$ is the angular velocity of the synchronous particle, i.e., if f

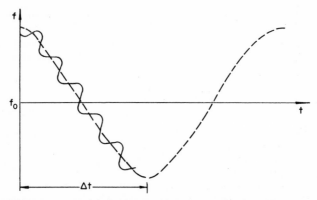

Fig. 6.1. Frequency modulation in a synchrocyclotron. The dashed line represents the variation of the radio frequency with time, the full line the variation of the frequency of revolution of a particle.

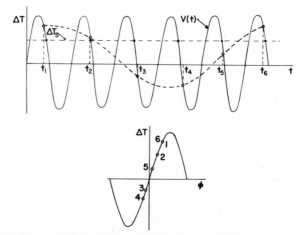

Fig. 6.2. Phase oscillations in the synchrocyclotron. (a) Energy gain per turn at different instants of time. The synchronous energy gain and the electric oscillation are also shown. (b) Energy gain per turn as a function of the phase. The numbers indicate the evolution of phase with time. Compare this figure with Fig. 4.3., depicting phase oscillations in modern linear accelerators.

is the radiofrequency, $\omega_s = 2\pi f$. The *phase* φ_s of the synchronous particle is defined by expressing its energy gain at each crossing of the accelerating gap between dees as $qV_{max} \sin \varphi_s$. Since there are two crossings per revolution, the energy gain per turn will be $2qV_{max} \sin \varphi_s$. In a similar way, we say that an arbitrary (non-synchronous) particle has the phase $\varphi = \varphi(t)$ at a certain time t if the energy gained when performing the revolution corresponding to that time is $2qV_{max} \sin \varphi$. As shown in Fig. 6.2, the phase is measured from the time at which the electric field passes through the value zero from an *accelerating* to a *decelerating* value, towards *decreasing* times. Note that with this definition, the phase differs by 90° from that used for the conventional cyclotron. Turning to Fig. 6.2, let us consider a particle which at time t has the same energy as the synchronous particle but a different phase, $\varphi_1 > \varphi_s$. Its energy gain will be therefore *greater* than that of the synchronous particle, and its angular velocity will become correspondingly *smaller*. In terms of the total energies, W and W_s,

$$\omega = qBc^2/W, \qquad \omega_s = qBc^2/W_s, \qquad (6.1)$$

where the subscript s always refers to the synchronous particle. Since $\omega_s > \omega$, the period of revolution will be *longer* than the synchronous period. The ion will arrive at the accelerating gap at a time t_2, when the accelerating voltage will be smaller than what it was at t_1, but with a phase φ_2 such that $\varphi_1 > \varphi_2 > \varphi_s$. Repetition of this process through successive turns will result in the total energy W becoming progressively greater than W_s, but by smaller amounts each time, and the phase becoming closer and closer to φ_s, until $\varphi = \varphi_s$. But although the phase may reach the synchronous value, W will still be greater than W_s and this brings about, as we have seen, a decrease in the value of the phase. A phase such that $\varphi < \varphi_s$ will thus be reached, where the ion gains energy at a slower rate than the synchronous particle, or even φ_3 in Fig. 6.2, where there is an energy loss instead of an energy gain. The process will continue until $W = W_s$. If this happens when $\varphi < \varphi_s$, in the next turn $W < W_s$, and the phase will stop decreasing and start increasing, thereby approaching again the synchronous value, whilst W will deviate even more from W_s until $\varphi = \varphi_s$ again. Then φ will start deviating from φ_s and W will approach W_s, and so forth. There is an oscillation of energies about the synchronous energy, associated with an oscillation of phases about the synchronous phase. The energy oscillations lag behind the phase oscillations by 90°, since $W - W_s$ is a maximum when $\varphi - \varphi_s = 0$ and vice versa.

In the above we have assumed that initially $W = W_s$. Since after a few turns the energy deviates from the synchronous value, the same reasoning applies when $W \neq W_s$ is taken as the initial condition. On the other hand, it is worth noting that the existence of phase and energy oscillations depends upon the synchronous phase being on the *decreasing* slope of the voltage. The reader may verify that, by similar arguments to those already given, a synchronous phase on the increasing slope, i.e., $\varphi_s > 90°$, leads to energies diverging from the synchronous value.

2. Phase Stability and Phase Oscillations

In order to gain a deeper insight into the mechanism of phase stability (or phase focussing, as it is also called), we shall proceed now to a more quantitative analysis. To begin with, we may point out that the above definition of phase coincides with the azimuthal angle of the particle with respect to the gap when the accelerating voltage is zero. Hence the change in phase, $d\varphi$, in a time dt, will be equal to the difference between the change in the azimuthal angle, $\omega\,dt$, and the change in phase of the voltage, that is, $\omega_s\,dt$, which is also the change in azimuthal angle of the synchronous particle. The resulting equation for the rate of change of the phase is

$$\frac{d\varphi}{dt} = \omega - \omega_s . \tag{6.2}$$

We shall find it convenient to take the azimuthal angle θ as the independent variable, instead of the time. In terms of this new variable,

$$\frac{d\varphi}{d\theta} = \frac{dt}{d\theta} \cdot \frac{d\varphi}{dt} = \frac{1}{\omega} \cdot \frac{d\varphi}{dt}$$

or

$$\frac{d\varphi}{d\theta} = 1 - \frac{\omega_s}{\omega} = 1 - \frac{W}{W_s} \tag{6.3}$$

where the right-hand side of the last equation results from replacing in eqn. (6.2) the values of ω and ω_s given by eqn. (6.1). We are neglecting the small difference in the fields corresponding to synchronous and non-synchronous particles. This is unimportant, since the *total* variation of the field may be of a few per cent from the centre to the final radius, whereas the final kinetic energy is, in a typical synchrocyclotron, about half the rest energy of the ions. It may be noted that the energy gain per unit angle is obtained by dividing the energy gain per turn (2π radians) by 2π. That is,

$$\frac{dW}{d\theta} = \frac{qV_{max}}{\pi} \sin \varphi . \tag{6.4}$$

Multiplying both sides of eqn. (6.3) by W_s and differentiating with respect to θ, we have, taking into account eqn. (6.4),

$$\frac{d}{d\theta} \left(W_s \frac{d\varphi}{d\theta} \right) = \frac{qV_{max}}{\pi} (\sin \varphi_s - \sin \varphi) . \tag{6.5}$$

This is the equation of phase oscillations and, if the angle is replaced by the time and the small variation of W_s with time is neglected, it is also the equation describing the motion of a pendulum acted upon by a constant torque, as illustrated in Fig. 6.3. In fact, if the pulley of radius a and the bar

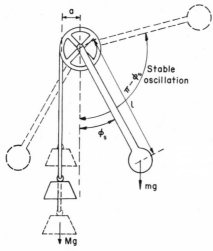

Fig. 6.3. Mechanical analogue of phase oscillations in a synchrocyclotron.

of length l supporting the weight mg are weightless, equating the rate of change of angular momentum with the moment of applied forces gives

$$(Ma^2 + ml^2) \frac{d^2\varphi}{dt^2} = Mga - mgl \sin \varphi . \tag{6.6}$$

This equation may be compared with the one resulting from (6.5) when W_s is assumed to be constant:

$$W_s \frac{d^2 \varphi}{d\theta^2} = \frac{qV_{max}}{\pi} \sin \varphi_s - \frac{qV_{max}}{\pi} \sin \varphi . \qquad (6.7)$$

The analogy is actually quite far-reaching. The equilibrium angle (or phase), about which oscillations are performed, is obtained from the condition that the moment of applied forces be zero, i.e.,

$$\sin \varphi = \sin \varphi_s = \frac{Ma}{ml} .$$

For an equilibrium position to exist at all, $\sin \varphi_s < 1$, that is, $Ma < ml$. If $\varphi_s = 90°$, $\sin \varphi_s = 1$ and the equilibrium is unstable; the slightest deviation results in the pendulum rotating around the suspension axis, the string in Fig. 6.3 unrolling from the pulley and the weight Mg falling down indefinitely. In a similar fashion, the choice of $\varphi_s = 90°$ in a synchrocyclotron would make the non-synchronous particles move continuously away (in phase) from the synchronous ions, and they would soon be out of step with the radio frequency.

How then is the optimum synchronous phase to be determined? The obvious answer is that the best value of φ_s is such that the largest number of ions performs stable phase oscillations about the synchronous phase, being thus driven towards the final energy. Returning to the pendulum model, a glance at Fig. 6.3 shows that it will undergo stable oscillations provided the angle $\pi - \varphi_s$ is not reached; this is a point of unstable equilibrium, beyond which the pendulum starts rotating as described above. This sets a limit to the largest possible stable phase oscillation and hence to the maximum phase difference between non-synchronous and synchronous particles such that the former still may be captured by the mechanism of phase stability. It would seem that a choice of $\varphi_s = 0$ (no constant torque acting on the pendulum) is most convenient, since then the oscillations would be stable in the interval $-\pi < \varphi < \pi$. But then half of the oscillation is performed with a negative phase, that is, losing instead of gaining energy. Even particles starting from the ion source with a positive phase will begin losing energy after a few turns and will return to the centre, becoming useless for acceleration.

A compromise between these two extremes ($\varphi_s = 0°$ and $\varphi_s = 90°$) seems to be desirable. We shall only outline here how this compromise is achieved. For a detailed account, the reader is referred to the papers by Bohm and Foldy (1946 and 1947). A first integration of the equation of phase oscillation in the form (6.7) can be readily performed if account is taken of the following mathematical identity:

$$\frac{d^2\varphi}{d\theta^2} = \frac{d\varphi}{d\theta}\frac{d}{d\varphi}\left(\frac{d\varphi}{d\theta}\right),$$

by means of which eqn. (6.7) is transformed into

$$\varphi'\frac{d\varphi'}{d\varphi} = \frac{qV_{max}}{\pi W_s}(\sin\varphi_s - \sin\varphi), \tag{6.8}$$

where primes have been used to denote derivatives with respect to θ. Now the left-hand side of this equation is just half the derivative of φ'^2 with respect to φ; integrating both sides gives

$$(\varphi')^2 = \frac{2qV_{max}}{\pi W_s}(\varphi\sin\varphi_s + \cos\varphi) + C$$

where the integration constant C has to be determined from the initial conditions. If φ_0 is the initial phase and φ'_0 the initial 'phase velocity',

$$(\varphi')^2 = \frac{2qV_{max}}{\pi W_s}[(\varphi - \varphi_0)\sin\varphi_s + \cos\varphi - \cos\varphi_0] + (\varphi'_0)^2. \tag{6.9}$$

Returning to the pendulum analogy, we have already seen that the maximum outward swing compatible with stable oscillations is that in which the pendulum stops just before reaching the point of unstability $\pi - \varphi_s$. For any given starting phase there will be a maximum starting velocity φ'_{0m} such that it will not bring the pendulum beyond that position. The condition is, therefore, that $\varphi' = 0$ for $\varphi = \pi - \varphi_s$. Furthermore, we can make use of the fact, already touched upon when dealing with the cyclotron, that the electric field bunches all the ions around the phase 90° during the first few turns, and take $\varphi_0 = 90°$. Replacing these values in eqn. (6.9), one obtains for the maximum phase velocity leading to stable oscillations,

$$(\varphi'_{0m})^2 = \frac{2qV_{max}}{\pi W_s}\left[\cos\varphi_s - \left(\frac{\pi}{2} - \varphi_s\right)\sin\varphi_s\right]. \tag{6.10}$$

But according to the eqn. (6.3) the phase velocity $\varphi' = (\omega - \omega_s)/\omega$ measures the discrepancy between the angular frequency of the ion and that of the synchronous particle. Since all the ions have the same angular frequency

$\omega_0 = qB/m_0$ at the centre, eqn. (6.10) just tells us how much the radio frequency may differ from ω_0 for a particle still to be caught into phase-stable oscillations. In other words, any particle starting from the ion source when the synchronous frequency is such that

$$\left(\frac{\omega_0 - \omega_s}{\omega_0}\right)^2 \leqslant (\varphi'_{0m})^2 \,, \tag{6.11}$$

will perform stable phase oscillations and will be accelerated to final energy. All the others will be lost. The efficiency of a synchrocyclotron will thus be proportional to the total range of frequencies in which capture into phase-stable motion is possible,

$$\Delta\omega_s = 2\omega_0 \varphi'_{0m} = 2\omega_0 \left\{\frac{2qV_{\max}}{\pi m_0 c^2} \left[\cos \varphi_s - \left(\frac{\pi}{2} - \varphi_s\right) \sin \varphi_s\right]\right\}^{\frac{1}{2}}, \tag{6.12}$$

where, since we are only concerned with the first few turns, we have taken $W_s = m_0 c^2$. It is clear that, once the frequency at the centre and the voltage are fixed, the efficiency is governed by the synchronous phase through the function

$$F(\varphi_s) = \pm \left[\cos \varphi_s - \left(\frac{\pi}{2} - \varphi_s\right) \sin \varphi_s\right]^{\frac{1}{2}}. \tag{6.13}$$

Curve I in Fig. 6.4 is a plot of this function. The question of whether an ion will return to the origin or not during the first phase oscillation depends on the rate of energy gain of the synchronous particle. In fact, one can regard the synchronous orbit as a circle expanding with increasing energy about which the non-synchronous orbit oscillates. If the increase in synchronous radius during the first phase oscillation is large enough to compensate for the 'shrinking' of the non-synchronous orbit corresponding to the minimum of energy oscillation, the ion will not return to the centre. Otherwise it will.

For $\varphi_s = 0$ there is no energy gain for the synchronous particle, so that all ions are lost. Incidentally, this is exactly the case of the conventional cyclotron. Ions do not return to the centre in this machine just because they reach the final energy before they can perform a complete phase oscillation. For small values of φ_s, particles starting when $\omega_s < \omega_0$ (that is to say, according to eqn. (6.2) with a positive phase velocity) take a longer time to reach the decelerating negative phases than those which start when $\omega_s > \omega_0$. In the former case the synchronous energy has a longer

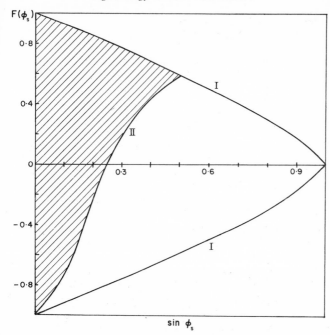

Fig. 6.4. Capture efficiency of a synchrocyclotron. Curve I is a plot of the function given by eqn. (6.13) in the text. Ions returning to the centre during the first phase oscillation are represented by the shaded region bounded by curves I and II.

time during which to increase before the orbit starts shrinking, so that these ions have a greater chance to survive. This is shown by curve II of Fig. 6.4; the shaded region corresponds to ions which return to the origin and are lost. It may be seen that the smallest phase for which no ions are lost in this way is $30°$. This is actually the most favourable phase, and is universally accepted in the design of synchrocyclotrons.

Fig. 6.5 shows the beam intensity as predicted by a combination of curves I and II of Fig. 6.4 and the experimental results obtained from a simulated synchrocyclotron in which the theory outlined above was tested for the first time. The machine was actually an old conventional cyclotron of small size (the diameter of the pole tips was 37 inches) in

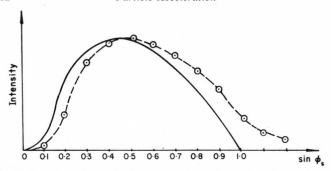

Fig. 6.5. Beam intensity obtained from a synchrocyclotron for different values of the synchronous phase. The theoretical predictions (full line) have been normalized to match the experimental point at $\varphi_s = 30°$. (After Bohm and Foldy, 1947).

which the magnetic field falloff was made artificially large to simulate the relativistic increase of mass at high energies through the decrease of the frequency of revolution.

We shall not dwell any longer on the mathematical analysis of phase motion, but merely quote some results concerning small phase oscillations. They can be obtained from eqn. (6.7) under the assumption that $\varphi - \varphi_s$ is a small quantity. The frequency of small phase oscillations, expressed as number of phase oscillations per unit angle of revolution of the particle is given by

$$\omega_\varphi = \left(\frac{qV_{\max} \cos \varphi_s}{\pi W_s}\right)^{\frac{1}{2}}, \tag{6.14}$$

and the amplitude of the phase oscillations is proportional to the quantity

$$W_s^{-\frac{3}{4}}(V_{\max} \cos \varphi_s)^{-\frac{1}{4}} \tag{6.15}$$

that is to say, it decreases as the energy increases. The amplitude of phase and energy oscillations is therefore damped. This implies that all particles surviving the first-phase oscillation will remain throughout the subsequent ones and will be accelerated to the final energy.

Besides the phase oscillations described above, particles in a synchrocyclotron suffer, as in all circular machines, the betatron oscillations touched upon when dealing with the standard cyclotron. The former are often referred to as longitudinal oscillations, as opposed to the latter, known as transverse oscillations. These two types of motion are very nearly independent, which justifies the separate treatments we have given to them.

3. Design of a Typical Synchrocyclotron

The formulae obtained above are basic in the design of synchrocyclotrons. Their use will become apparent by means of a numerical example. Let us consider the design of a synchrocyclotron accelerating protons up to 500 MeV. The increase in mass resulting from this kinetic energy is 53·2 per cent (the rest mass of the proton is 938 MeV). This implies that the use of relativistic formulae is compulsory, as it was in the case of the betatron. Assuming a magnetic field of 20 000 gauss (2 weber/m^2) at maximum radius, this radius is, according to eqn. (5.27)

$$R = \frac{(1438^2 - 938^2)^{\frac{1}{2}} 10^6}{3 \times 10^8 \times 2} = 1·82 \text{ metres} ,$$

since the total energy is $938 + 500 = 1\,438$ MeV. The diameter of the pole tips will be therefore of about 4 metres. The magnetic field fall-off with radius is no longer a cause, as it was in the case of the standard cyclotron, of loss of synchronism; it may have a relatively large value, say 5 per cent. The resulting field at the centre will then be 21 000 gauss, which is about the maximum allowed by good-quality iron. Equation (6.1) with $W = 938$ MeV yields for the angular frequency at the centre $20·1 \times 10^7$ radians per second, corresponding to a radio frequency of 32·1 Mc/s. The same equation with $W = 1\,438$ MeV gives a final angular frequency of $12·6 \times 10^7$ radians per second and a radio frequency of 20 Mc/s. The frequency modulation is usually achieved by means of a rotating condenser, consisting of a cog-wheel spinning between two concentric rings, with teeth corresponding to those in the wheel. The rings and the wheel form the two plates of a condenser in the electronic circuit which generates the radio frequency, whose capacity varies according as to whether the teeth in the wheel face those in the rings or not. The change in capacity brings about the required change in electric frequency.

Next we have to consider the voltage between the dees. Thanks to phase stability, the requirements are not as stringent as for the conventional cyclotron. A peak voltage of 15 kilovolts is sufficient for the machine we are considering. We can dispense with the need of two insulated dees: one of them will carry the full voltage, and the other will be just a piece of copper connected to ground, called the dummy dee, having a profile similar to that of the real dee. With a synchronous phase $\varphi_s = 30°$, the energy gain per turn will be $2qV_{max} \sin \varphi_s = 15$ keV. Full energy will be attained after $500/0·015 = 33\,440$ turns or, since the frequency of revolution corresponding to the average energy is 29·4 Mc/s, after $33\,440/(29·4 \times 10^6)$ $= 1·14 \times 10^{-3}$ seconds. The rate of frequency change will be therefore $10\,650$ Mc/s^2; this quantity actually fixes the value of the synchronous phase, which thus depends, in the end, upon the frequency of revolution and the spacing between teeth in the rotating condenser.

If the values $\varphi_s = 30°$, $qV_{max} = 15$ keV and $f_0 = \omega_0/2\pi = 32·1$ Mc/s are replaced in eqn. (6.12) it will be seen that the frequency range for capture into phase-stable motion is 0·122 Mc/s. In other words, only those ions starting from the ion source while the radio frequency is between 32·161 Mc/s and 32·039 Mc/s will survive all phase oscillations and will attain the final energy of 500 MeV. The above frequency change will be accomplished in $0·122/10\,650 = 11·4$ microseconds, which is 1 per cent of the time required for acceleration.

Once the frequency has reached its minimum value, corresponding to the final energy, it has to increase again, as shown in Fig. 6.1, to start a new cycle of acceleration. This takes about the same time as the decrease, but is useless for acceleration. The beam from a synchrocyclotron appears in the form of short bursts (in our example lasting 11·4 microseconds) separated by time intervals during which either the frequency increases or a new bunch of ions is being accelerated. In the machine we are considering these blank periods will last not less than 2 280 microseconds, which implies a duty cycle of 0·5 per cent.

As to the phase oscillations, a straightforward application of eqn. (6.14) tells us that a single phase (or energy) oscillation will require 475 turns at the beginning of the acceleration ($W_s = 938$ MeV) and 590 near the final energy ($W_s = 1\,438$ MeV). According to eqn. (6.15) the amplitude of the last oscillation will be 73 per cent of the amplitude near the centre of the machine.

There are about twenty synchrocyclotrons operating in different countries; the characteristic features of a few of them are listed in Table 6.1.

It can be seen that these machines cover a wide range of energies and sizes; their applications and use will vary accordingly. The higher-energy machines, for example, are useful tools in the investigation of the properties of elementary particles. Protons above 200 MeV can produce, after inter-action with a target, secondary beams of fast mesons which in turn can be used as projectiles impinging on nucleons. An example of the kind of installations used in these experiments has already been given in Fig. 1.3.

TABLE 6.1
Characteristics of some Synchrocyclotrons

Location	Pole diameter (m)	Energy (MeV)	Magnet weight (tons)	Magnetic field (kilogauss)
California (U.S.A.)	4·80	730	4 000	23·3
Dubna (U.S.S.R.)	6·00	680	7 200	16·8
Geneva (Switzerland)	5·00	600	2 500	18·9
Liverpool (U.K.)	3·95	400	1 640	18·9
Uppsala (Sweden)	2·30	200	600	21·5
Orsay (France)	2·80	155	650	16·3
Amsterdam (Holland)	1·80	28	200	14·0
Buenos Aires (Argentina)	1·80	28	196	14·6

The intermediate-energy machines (100 to 200 MeV) have been extremely valuable in the study of nucleon-nucleon interactions and the structure of the nucleus. For example, a promising new field has been recently opened by the so-called 'quasi-free proton scattering' or (p, 2p) reactions. In these processes an incident high-energy proton strikes off the target nucleus one of its protons, both particles leaving the nucleus almost seemingly 'unaware', of what has happened. The energy and angular correlation between the outgoing protons yield important information about the momentum of the struck proton prior to the reaction, making it thus possible to investigate the distribution of momenta far inside the nucleus. As to the lower-energy machines, their applications overlap up to a certain point with those of standard cyclotrons and proton linear accelerators, being mainly devoted to nuclear scattering and reaction studies. Some of them, in spite of their low beam currents as compared with conventional cyclotrons, are also employed in the production of radioisotopes.

Synchrocyclotrons are, in a certain sense, technically outdated machines.

Azimuthally-varying-field cyclotrons, to be dealt with in Chapter 7, should in principle be able to deliver high intensity beams (continuous rather than pulsed) of the same energy as synchrocyclotrons. Moreover, their magnets require less iron and are therefore cheaper than those of synchrocyclotrons, but the attainment of magnetic fields of the desired shape poses extremely difficult problems.

4. The Electron Synchrotron

When studying the betatron we found that the maximum energy attainable was limited mainly because of the very low (a few electron-volts) energy gain per turn. At high energies this gain is compensated by the losses due to electromagnetic radiation, making any further acceleration impossible. An obvious way out of this difficulty would be to install an accelerating space (for example a resonating cavity) supplying the energy gain when betatron operation is no longer possible. The resulting machine is the electron synchrotron. Acceleration is provided by one or more accelerating stations along the orbit, which is kept fixed by a guiding magnetic field. The field strength is periodically raised from low to high values, the former being used for injection of relatively low-energy electrons. Energy gains per turn of about a thousand times those achieved in the betatron can be easily obtained in this way. But, since the energy gain is not connected with the rate of change of the flux linked by the orbit, the magnetic field likewise need not fulfil any longer the relation (5.25). Of course, a necessary condition for this type of acceleration is the existence of some sort of phase stability if high energies are to be reached. We shall now discuss how this condition can be established in the machine described above.

Let us recall that the velocity of electrons moving with kinetic energies of about 2 MeV, is so close to that of light that it does not increase appreciably under further energy gains. If the electrons are going to move on an orbit of fixed radius (as they do in the electron synchrotron) and hence of fixed length, their frequency of revolution will be practically the same, no matter how much greater than 2 MeV their energy may be. The frequency is given by

$$f = \frac{c}{2\pi r_0} = \frac{47 \cdot 8}{r_0} \, \text{Mc/s} \,, \tag{6.16}$$

where the radius of the orbit, r_0, should be expressed in metres. The condition of synchronism, therefore, requires that the electric frequency should have the same (constant) value. How then, in the absence of frequency modulation, is the synchronous particle to be defined? The answer is straightforward if one recalls the relation between the angular frequency, the magnetic field and the total energy,

$$\omega_s = qBc^2/W_s, \tag{6.17}$$

where, as usual, the subscript s denotes synchronous particles. In the synchrocyclotron the nature of the particles (ions) was such that their acceleration entailed a decrease of their frequency of revolution in the presence of a practically constant magnetic field. Conversely, since relativistic electrons revolve on a fixed orbit with constant frequency, the synchronous energy can only increase with time in the electron synchrotron if the magnetic field is also made to increase so as to satisfy eqn. (6.17). These are just the conditions of operation of the electron synchrotron, thus warranting the existence of the synchronous particle and phase stability. In other words, the actual mechanism (decrease of radio frequency, increase of magnetic field, or both) through which synchronism is achieved is unimportant. Provided this mechanism corresponds to the nature of the particles to be accelerated, phase focussing will be established. The reader may verify that the whole theory developed above for phase oscillations and stability in the synchrocyclotron is based only upon (a) the existence of a synchronous phase and (b) the fact that the rate of change of the non-synchronous phase is given by eqn. (6.2). All the previous results are therefore immediately applicable to the electron synchrotron and to any other machine in which the frequency and the field satisfy eqn. (6.17) with increasing synchronous energy.

In the case of electrons, however, another complication is added to the picture, although it does not introduce any essentially new results: the emission of radiation by the accelerated particles. This effect, negligible when dealing with ions, brings about a strong damping of the phase oscillations of relativistic electrons. One would expect the output beam of a synchrotron to consist of very short pulses in which the electrons should be densely concentrated around the synchronous phase. This result follows from the classical electromagnetic theory of light emission, and gives a valid description of the *average* behaviour of the electrons; but according to the quantum theory, emission takes place in discrete steps, resulting in statistical deviations from the classical average. Consider for example an individual electron, very close, in phase and energy, to the synchronous particle: after losing energy through the emission of a light quantum it suddenly will find itself—energy- and frequency-wise—out of step with the synchronous particle. This results in a rapid change of phase, whereby new phase oscillations are induced. The outcome is an additional spread of the packet, which often compensates the classical bunching of the phase oscillations.

5. Radiation Effects in Electron Synchrotrons

Radiation losses are important in another respect, namely, in setting a limit to the energies attainable in practice with electron synchrotrons. According to the electromagnetic theory of radiation, the total energy emitted per turn by an electron of kinetic energy T is

$$\Delta E_r = \frac{4}{3} \pi \frac{q^2}{r} \left(\frac{W}{mc^2} \right)^4 = 8 \cdot 9 \times 10^{-14} \frac{W^4}{v} \tag{6.18}$$

where the energies are measured in MeV and r, the radius of the orbit, in metres. Let us consider two synchrotrons, one with final energy $T_f = 500$ MeV and the other with $T_f = 1 \cdot 5$ GeV. Since in both cases the kinetic energy is much larger than the rest energy (0·51 MeV), we can write

$$W \simeq T \simeq pc = qBrc \tag{6.19}$$

where p is the linear momentum of the particle. Assuming a maximum field strength of 12 kilogauss ($1 \cdot 2$ weber/m^2) the radius will be $1 \cdot 39$ m in the first case and $4 \cdot 17$ m in the second. Straightforward application of formula (6.18) yields energy losses per turn of 4 keV and 107 keV, respectively. These are minimum values for the accelerating voltages if they must overcome the radiation losses.

It is interesting to work out the ratio between the total energy lost through radiation and the kinetic energy stored in the beam. This can be done by assuming a sinusoidal dependence of the field on time, $B = B_{max} \sin \Omega t$, and integrating (6.18) with respect to time with the aid of (6.19), for the time interval in which B increases, i.e., from $t = 0$ to $t = \pi/(2\Omega)$. The result is

$$\varepsilon = \frac{E_r}{T_f} = 2 \cdot 5 \times 10^{-6} \frac{T_f^3}{\Omega r^2}. \tag{6.20}$$

The energies being measured in MeV and the radius in metres. It is obviously desirable to make Ω as large as possible, to minimize this ratio. Furthermore, a high frequency of the alternating magnetic field implies a high repetition rate and consequently high beam intensity. The mains frequency, 50 cycles per second, is a practical value. With this value, the efficiency defined as

$$\frac{T_f}{T_f + E_r} = \frac{1}{1 + E_r/T_f},$$

is 66 per cent for the 500-MeV machine and 39·5 per cent for the 1·5-GeV machine. The last value is by no means untypical, although it could be made better by choosing a larger radius. For instance, a radius of 7·2 m (requiring a maximum field of 6 900 gauss at 1·5 GeV) would give an efficiency of 66 per cent, the same as the smaller machine.

The choice of accelerating voltage and synchronous phase is also governed by considerations of the radiation losses. The definition of synchronous phase must be modified to take them into account. If qV_{max} is the maximum possible energy gain per turn,

$$qV_{max} \sin \varphi_s = \Delta T_s + \Delta E_{rs}, \qquad (6.21)$$

where ΔT_s is the actual energy gain per turn of the synchronous particle and ΔE_{rs} its radiation loss per turn. The rate of change with time can be obtained by multiplying the above expression by $\omega_s/(2\pi)$ (i.e., the number of turns per unit time), giving

$$\frac{\omega_s}{2\pi} qV_{max} \sin \varphi_s - \frac{dE_{rs}}{dt} = \frac{dT_s}{dt} = T_f \Omega \cos \Omega t,$$

where the right-hand side follows from eqn. (6.19) and the assumed sinusoidal variation of the magnetic field. At the beginning of the acceleration cycle ($t \simeq 0$) the radiation losses are negligible, so that

$$qV_{max} \sin \varphi_s = 2\pi r T_f \Omega/c .$$

By replacing the appropriate numerical values one finds that the required energy gain will be 4·55 keV per turn in the smaller machine and 40·7 keV in the larger one. By the end of the acceleration cycle ($\Omega t = \pi/2$) $dT_s/dt = 0$, and the accelerating voltage need only compensate for the radiation losses which were found to be 4 keV and 107 keV, respectively. This implies that the radio-frequency voltage may be roughly constant during acceleration in the first machine, with the synchronous phase being also nearly constant. Since radiation-induced phase oscillations may become quite important at a few hundred MeV, it is convenient to choose a small synchronous phase, for example $\varphi_s = 30°$, to allow an ample range of stable phase oscillations. With this choice, $qV_{max} = 8$ keV. The value of $qV_{max} \sin \varphi_s$ goes from 40·7 keV to 107 keV in the 1·5-GeV machine. It is clear that V_{max} and φ_s cannot be both constant. On the other hand, the phase oscillations become so strongly damped at high energies that values of φ_s as high as 60° or 70° can be employed without appreciable loss of beam. It may be advantageous, therefore, to let φ_s vary gradually from small values at low energy to angles near 90° at full energy, by making the radio frequency voltage constant. In our case, we may take $\varphi_s = 60°$ at the end of the acceleration cycle, which implies $qV_{max} = 124$ keV, and $\varphi_s = 20°$ at the beginning of the cycle.

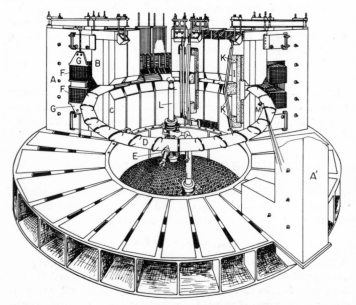

Fig. 6.6. Cut-away drawing of the Cornell University 300-MeV synchrotron.
(A) Magnet C-section; (A') oversize C-section providing exit space for the beam; (B) and (C) upper and lower pole pieces; (D) vacuum chamber; (E) electron gun; (F) magnet coils; (G) supports for the coils; (I) magnetic shunts, or flux bars, across pole gaps; (K) insulating blocks holding the flux bars against the poles; (L) vacuum pumps; (M) internal target. (*By courtesy of Dr. R. R. Wilson*)

The two machines could be taken as examples of earlier and more recent trends in synchrotron design. The 500-MeV accelerators would still be very similar to a betatron and would indeed operate as one during part of the acceleration cycle. The single massive magnet would be replaced by several C-shaped iron frames, as shown in Fig. 6.6, creating the field in a small region around the circular equilibrium orbit. Electrons would be injected at about 100 keV by means of an electron gun into a doughnut-shaped acceleration chamber, as in a betatron. The changing magnetic flux in the interior of the orbit required for induction acceleration would be provided by flux iron bars, as shown in Fig. 6.6, which saturate for fields corresponding to energies of about 10 MeV. In our case this energy is reached after 66 microseconds, with a field of 250 gauss. The radio frequency is then turned on for the rest of the cycle. The acceleration cycle is schematically illustrated in Fig. 6.7.

In the higher-energy machine we could adopt a race-track layout, with magnets in four circular quadrants separated by four straight field-free sections. These field-free regions would accommodate the accelerating cavities (more than one will be needed to provide the required energy gain per turn), vacuum pumps, targets, extraction systems, etc. We should give up the betatron stage altogether, and replace it by a frequency-modulated accelerating gap, operating until the electrons reach fully relativistic energies. At this time a fixed-frequency oscillator would be switched on, carrying the electrons to final energy. Alternatively, one could attempt the injection of the electrons directly at high energy by means of a 3-MeV

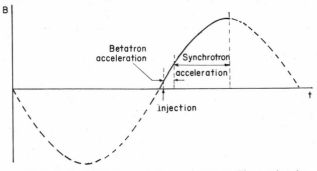

Fig. 6.7. Magnetic field cycle in an electron synchrotron. The acceleration part of the cycle is shown as a full line.

Van de Graaff generator or, if higher initial energies are necessary, a 10-MeV linear accelerator.

Betatron oscillations are, of course, also present in electron synchrotrons. Since the particles do not start from the centre, they do not need to pass over 'dangerous' values of the field index n such as 0.2 or 0.5, where radial and vertical oscillations couple. A typical value is $n = 0.6$, as in the betatron.

Usually the electron beam is allowed to strike a target located in the acceleration chamber, yielding an intense beam of energetic gamma-rays. This secondary beam is in turn used to induce, for example, photonuclear reactions, in which one or more nucleons are struck off a nucleus by an incident gamma-photon. The target is generally on the inside of the equilibrium orbit; the accelerating voltage is turned off when the electrons have slightly more than the desired energy, so that the radiation loss makes the orbit shrink to a smaller radius, where the electrons hit the target.

6. The Proton Synchrotron

Synchrocyclotrons can in principle yield particles of any desired energy. This fact does not imply that other means of heavy-particle acceleration should be discarded. On the contrary, there exist strong economical reasons to encourage the use of other machines. The radius of a cyclotron magnet increases as the square root of the kinetic energy for non-relativistic velocities and linearly with energy for velocities close to that of light. As the weight of the magnet is roughly proportional to the third power of the radius, it can be concluded that the cost of a high-energy synchrocyclotron (mainly determined by the size of the magnet) is approximately proportional to the cube of the kinetic energy reached.

It is clear that acceleration on a fixed orbit, as in the electron synchrotron, would change this cubic dependence into a linear one. This would be extremely convenient for kinetic energies beyond the semirelativistic region, that is, a few times the rest energy of the particles.

The proton synchrotron is the machine generally used for the production of proton beams in the GeV energy range. Its name does not imply that its principles of operation apply exclusively to protons (they are equally valid for deuterons, alpha-particles or other ions), but results from the fact that protons, being elementary particles themselves, are preferred for investigations in elementary particle physics.

The proton machines are in certain respects straightforward extensions of electron synchrotrons. The magnetic field is established over an annular region, occupied by a doughnut-shaped acceleration chamber (Fig. 6.8), and increases with time during acceleration, so as to keep the protons revolving on a fixed orbit. The protons are accelerated to a few MeV and then injected into the machine. They are subsequently accelerated by radio-frequency fields which must be synchronized with the revolution frequency of the particles in the changing magnetic field. When the protons have reached the desired energy they are either made to strike an internal target or extracted from the machine.

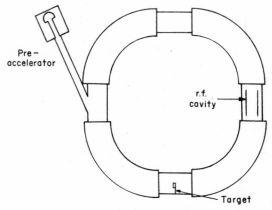

Fig. 6.8. Schematic diagram of a proton synchrotron.

Differences between electron and proton synchrotrons arise from the difference in the masses of the particles. The much heavier protons only acquire a velocity close to that of light near the end of the acceleration cycle. The frequency of revolution around the fixed orbit must therefore increase with time, until it reaches a saturation value given by eqn. (6.16). The accelerating radio frequency has to be correspondingly modulated to maintain synchronism, as illustrated in Fig. 6.9. On the other hand, radiation losses are hardly significant in the proton case, and need not be taken into account in the design of a machine.

The cost of a proton synchrotron may seem formidable, but it is, in a

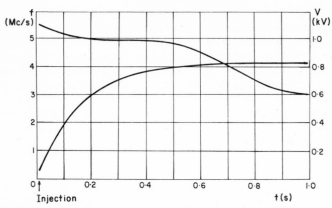

Fig. 6.9. Variations of voltage and radio frequency during the acceleration cycle
in the Cosmotron.

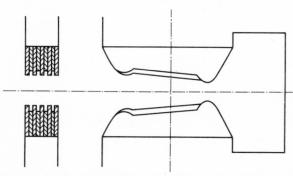

Fig. 6.10. Crenelated pole arrangement to produce a constant field index for a
range of values of the field.

sense, the most economical machine known at present. The first one to
operate, the Brookhaven Cosmotron (Cosmotron Staff, 1953), required
an investment of six million dollars to produce 3-GeV protons. This
implies a cost of 0·2 cents per electron-volt, which compares very favourably with the 8 cents per electron-volt of a Van de Graaff generator. Of
course, comparisons of this sort cannot be pushed very far because both
machines differ so widely in their applications.

The first proposal of a fixed-orbit, annular-field accelerator with simultaneous variation of magnetic field and radio frequency was made in 1943 by M. L. Oliphant, then at Birmingham University. War secrecy prevented its publication until 1947, when the independent papers by Veksler in the U.S.S.R. and McMillan in the U.S.A. describing the principle of phase stability and its application to machines such as the electron and proton synchrotrons, had already appeared.

We shall deal here with the so-called weak focussing or constant gradient synchrotrons. Radial and vertical stability of the orbits is achieved by means of a field slowly decreasing with increasing radius. Hence the field not only has to increase with time but must also keep a constant shape during the acceleration cycle. This poses an extremely severe condition, which can only be approximately fulfilled through much technical ingenuity. Fig. 6.10 shows how the field index is kept nearly constant in a model for the Saclay 3-GeV synchrotron: the pole tips are formed by alternate laminations of different profile. The protruding laminations govern the shape of the field at low intensities, whereas at high intensities they saturate and the field is mainly determined by the lower laminations, of different shape. In this way the magnetic field is usable up to 15 kG.

The ions must be accelerated up to a few MeV before injection, and their entrance must be accurately timed so that they encounter the required field, usually of a few hundred gauss. Pre-acceleration is performed by a Linac in the largest machines, but the Cosmotron uses a Van de Graaff and the Birmingham synchrotron a Cockcroft-Walton generator.

The beam is properly orientated into the acceleration chamber by a device called an 'inflector', shown in Fig. 6.11. It consists of two metallic plates between which a strong electric field is established. The particles pass through this field and leave it with trajectories practically parallel to the equilibrium orbit.

We have already said that the radio frequency must increase with time if it is to match the motion of the particles. From the expression for the total energy,

$$W = W_0/(1 - v^2/c^2)^{\frac{1}{2}},$$

the value of the velocity can be found to be

$$v = c(1 - W_0^2/W^2)^{\frac{1}{2}}.$$

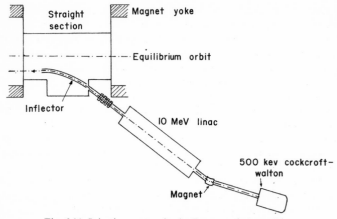

Fig. 6.11. Injection system in the Bevatron (schematic).

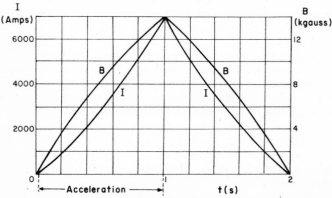

Fig. 6.12. Magnetic field and coil current variation in the Cosmotron during the acceleration cycle.

Now, if the particles are constrained to move on the same orbit of radius r_s their angular velocity will be

$$\omega_s = v_s/r_s = c(1 - W_0^2/W_s^2)^{\frac{1}{2}}/r_s, \quad (6.22)$$

where the subscript s denotes, as usual, synchronous values. Replacing eqn. (6.1) for W_s in (6.22) the dependence of the radio frequency upon the magnetic field can be obtained,

$$f = \omega_s/2\pi = (c/2\pi r_s)/[1 + W_0^2/(qBr_sc)^2]^{\frac{1}{2}} . \tag{6.23}$$

The radio frequency must be programmed to follow this expression as closely as possible.

We have taken for granted the existence of a synchronous phase, and therefore, phase stability. We now proceed to show that this is indeed the case. In fact, a combination of eqns. (6.1) and (6.22) (or alternatively, eqn. (5.27)) yields

$$(W_s^2 - W_0^2)^{\frac{1}{2}} = qBr_sc .$$

Differentiating this equation with respect to time we obtain,

$$\frac{dW_s}{dt} = \frac{qr_sc}{W_s}(W_s^2 - W_0^2)^{\frac{1}{2}}\frac{dB}{dt} = qr_s^2\omega_s\frac{dB}{dt} .$$

The energy gain per turn will be equal to the time derivative of W_s times the time required to perform one turn, i.e.,

$$\Delta W_s = \frac{2\pi}{\omega_s}\frac{dW_s}{dt} = 2\pi qr_s^2\frac{dB}{dt} = qV_{\max}\sin\varphi_s , \tag{6.24}$$

where the right-hand side defines the synchronous phase. Equation (6.24) shows that a constant voltage will produce a constant synchronous phase only if the field increases linearly with time during the acceleration cycle, that is, $(dB/dt) =$ constant. In practice, a pattern of field variation like that of Fig. 6.12 is obtained, and deviations from linear behaviour must be compensated by changes of the accelerating voltage, as shown in Fig. 6.9, to keep the synchronous phase constant. Again, the time rate of change of the non-synchronous phase is given by the difference between the non-synchronous values of the angular velocity. We are thus led back to eqn. (6.2), from which all the results concerning phase oscillations followed.

The acceleration cycle may take between one and three seconds. During this time the protons travel along a distance equal to a few times the circumference of the earth (twenty times in the Synchrophasotron). Even at pressures as low as 10^{-6} mm Hg there is a high probability that the particles collide with molecules of residual gas. This results in induced betatron oscillations which may bring about the loss of a certain fraction of the beam through hitting the walls of the vacuum chamber.

Fig. 6.13. Sectional drawing of the Bevatron and ancillary equipment. (*Courtesy of Lawrence Radiation Laboratory*). (1) Cockcroft-Walton accelerator; (2) linear accelerator; (3) accelerator magnet; (4) accelerator tank; (5) concrete shielding; (6) control room; (7) counting room; (8) lobby and display; (9) experimental area; (10) secondary beams; (11) external proton beam; (12) generator room.

TABLE 6.2
Constant Gradient Synchrotrons

Name	Cosmotron	Birmingham	Bevatron	Synchro-phasotron	Saturne	Princeton	Nimrod	ZGS
Location Date of operation	Brookhaven 1952	Birmingham 1953	Berkeley 1954	Dubna 1957	Saclay 1958	Princeton 1964	Harwell 1964	Argonne 1964
Max. energy (GeV)	3	1	6·2	10	3	3	7	12·5
Orbit radius (m)	9·14	4·50	15·24	28	11	12·2	23·6	27·4
Number of straight sections	4	0	4	4	4	16	8	8
Weight of iron (tons)	1650	800	9700	36000	1080	350	7000	4000
Beam pulses per minute	12	6	10	5	19	1140	28	15
Max. field (kG)	13·8	12·6	15·4	13	15	13·8	14	21·5
Injection energy (MeV)	3·6	0·46	9·9	9	3·6	3	15	50
Number of accelerating stations	1	1	1	2	1	4	1	2
Vacuum chamber Width (cm)	91	50	122	150	60	18	91	81
Height (cm)	22	21	30	40	10	7	24	15

In spite of the complexities inherent to such an installation (see Fig. 6.13) the rather large number of ten weak-focussing proton synchrotrons are now (1965) either in operation or under construction. In 1952 the 'Cosmotron' at the Brookhaven National Laboratory (U.S.A.) was the first one to deliver a high energy proton/beam. The largest (in size) in operation is the 10-GeV 'Synchrophasotron' at the Joint Institute for Nuclear Research, Dubna (U.S.S.R.), although the honour of the highest energy belongs to the 12·5-GeV machine at the Argonne National Laboratory (U.S.A.). The latter is a zero-gradient $(n=0)$ synchrotron, to be dealt with in the next section.

Other operating machines are the Birmingham synchrotron (1 GeV), the only one with a completely circular shape, the 6·2-GeV Berkeley Bevatron (U.S.A.), the 3-GeV 'Saturne' synchrotron at the Centre d'Études Nucléaires de Saclay (France) and the 7-GeV 'Nimrod', at the Atomic Energy Research Establishment (Harwell, Great Britain). The rapid-cycling synchrotron at Princeton University (U.S.A.), is a machine of recent construction (1965). Its main feature is the high intensity of its 3-GeV beam, obtained through a fast repetition rate of 19 cycles per second.

The design features of some of the above-mentioned proton synchrotrons may be found in Table 6.2.

7. The ZGS

The above initials refer to the Zero-Gradient Synchrotron, built by the Argonne National Laboratory in the United States. Its unique feature is a value of the field index $n=0$, implying a uniform field inside the magnet gap. One would expect neither radial nor vertical focussing in such a field. In fact, both types of focussing result from the fringe fields *outside* the eight sections that form the ring magnet in this machine.

Let us study first the wedge magnets that have been used for many years in the analysis of beams containing particles of various energies. They take advantage of the fact that the trajectories of particles with different momenta have different radii of curvature in a magnetic field. Upon entering a magnetic sector they travel along different paths, as shown in Fig. 6.14. A slit located in the field-free region allows the passage of particles with the desired energy. Moreover, a magnetic sector has focussing properties, in the sense that particles of the same momentum diverging away from a point source, such as 1 and 2 in Fig. 6.14, converge

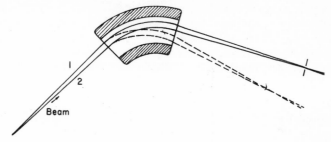

Fig. 6.14. A magnetic sector as an energy analyzer: particles of different energies (full and dashed lines) are focussed on different points after traversing the field.

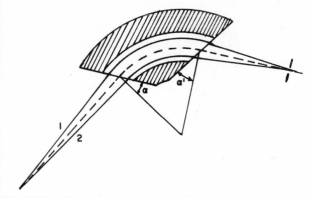

Fig. 6.15. Reinforcement of the focussing effect of a magnetic sector by proper slanting of the pole ends with respect to the beam.

on a point after traversing the magnet. The reason for this behaviour lies in the fact that particle 1 travels along a slightly longer path, and therefore suffers a slightly larger deflection in the magnetic field than the central ray. The reverse is true for particle 2. Apart from the bending of trajectories, a magnetic sector behaves with respect to particle rays in the same way as a thick lens behaves regarding light rays in optics.

So far, we have considered the case where the ion trajectory is normal to the boundaries of the field. A slanting of the pole ends such as shown in Fig. 6.15 would result in an even longer path for particle 1 and shorter

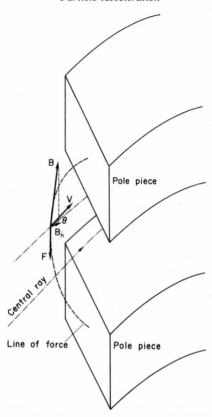

Fig. 6.16. Vertical focussing produced by the fringe field of a magnet. The horizontal component B_h forms an angle θ with the velocity of a particle, v. If the velocity is not normal to the pole end this results in a vertical force F acting on the particle.

path for particle 2, reinforcing the focussing effect in the horizontal plane. Conversely, the effect can be made weaker by reversing the inclination of the pole boundaries. But in this case an interesting feature is introduced, namely, vertical focussing by the fringe fields at the boundaries. Consider

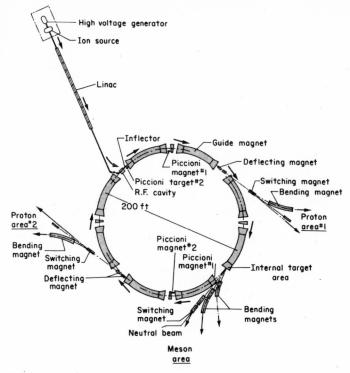

Fig. 6.17. Plan view of the Zero Gradient Synchrotron, showing the history of a particle. Piccioni targets and magnets assist in the process of beam extraction. (*By courtesy of Dr. A. V. Crewe, Argonne National Laboratory*).

a particle leaving or entering the magnet above the median plane*
(Fig. 6.16). Since the barrel-shaped lines of force lie on planes perpendicular to the pole boundaries, the horizontal component of the fringe field has in turn a non-zero component normal to the particle trajectory. The

---

* The median plane is, by definition, the locus of the points where the only non-zero component of the field is the vertical one. In this discussion we assume that the central ray lies on a horizontal plane.

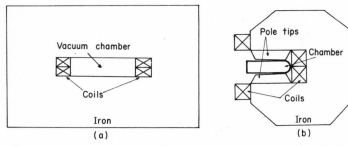

Fig. 6.18. Distribution of iron and coils in the magnets of the ZGS (*a*) and in the C-shaped magnets of Saturne (*b*).

resulting vertical force is opposed to the deviation of the particle from the median plane, providing therefore the required focussing effect. The reader may verify that a similar conclusion is reached for a particle moving below the median plane.

The sections of the ZGS (Fig. 6.17) are just double focussing magnets of this type. In a 'classical' ($n \simeq 0.6$) machine the requirement of constant field index sets a limit of about 15 kG to the maximum field attainable, but in the ZGS the maximum field is 21·5 kG. A higher field implies a smaller radius and a smaller amount of iron in the magnet; the economy in this design becomes apparent recalling that the magnet of the Synchrophasotron weighs 36 000 tons, whereas the 12·5-GeV ZGS has a magnet which weighs only 4 000 tons. The magnetic sections in the ZGS have 'window frame' or poleless structure, enabling very high uniform fields to be obtained. They are shown in Fig. 6.18, together with the 'C'-shaped magnets usual in most synchrotrons.

The ZGS is a high-intensity machine: it delivers 15 beam bursts per minute, which compares favourably with the rates of other synchrotrons. The acceleration cycle takes one second, followed by a blank period of three seconds during which the field returns to zero. This performance is only surpassed by the much smaller (3 GeV) Princeton machine, whose repetition rate is 19 cycles per second.

8. Beam Extraction from High-Energy Machines

The extraction of the beam from a synchrotron or synchrocyclotron is a complicated technical problem. In synchrocyclotrons, for example, the simple electrical deflector arrangement used in conventional cyclotron must be discarded, because of the small separation between successive orbits. Using the relativistic equation (5.27) one finds, for the radius increase Δr corresponding to an increase ΔT of the kinetic energy:

$$\frac{\Delta r}{r} = \frac{1 + T/W_0}{2 + T/W_0} \frac{\Delta T}{T},$$

which, in the case of the 500-MeV synchrocyclotron described in Section 3 yields an orbit separation per turn of $3 \cdot 3 \times 10^{-3}$ cm. This is much smaller than the amplitude of the radial oscillations performed by the particles about their equilibrium orbit. In fact, the actual orbits intermingle and there is no clearcut separation between them. The interposition of a thin septum is out of the question.

The simplest method of beam deflection is the interception of the internal beam by a thin target made of a material of high atomic number, such as uranium. The particles are scattered in all directions, and a small fraction (about $0 \cdot 1\%$) may reach the mouth of a magnetic channel where they are subjected to a reduced field until they leave the machine. The internal target is also used for the production of secondary particles, such as mesons, which result from the interaction of the primary beam with matter.

Another more efficient procedure consists of inducing forced radial oscillations on the orbits. To this end a magnetic perturbation produced by suitably shaped iron blocks (regenerator) is made to alter the cylindrical symmetry of the field. The regenerator reinforces the field in a narrow angular zone (Fig. 6.19) starting at a radius r_0, known as the extraction radius. For $r < r_0$ the regenerator field must be zero, increasing with radius for $r > r_0$. In this way the particles proceed unperturbed until they reach the orbit of radius r_0. Most of them perform stable betatron oscillations about their equilibrium orbits. These oscillations, as we know, (cf. eqn. (5.21)) have a frequency smaller than that of a revolution. In other words, it takes more than one turn of the particle to perform a complete radial oscillation (according to eqn. (5.21) it takes an angle $2\pi/(1-n)^{\frac{1}{2}} \simeq 2\pi + n\pi$). This means that, as shown in Fig. 6.19, the actual trajectory of the particle is a sort of 'rosette', whose nodes (points where the trajectory intersects the circular equilibrium orbit) precess with time. Since in the regenerator zone the field is stronger than in the rest of the magnet gap, the path will be bent inwards with respect to the 'natural' path in the

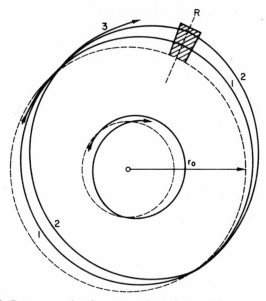

Fig. 6.19. Beam extraction from a synchrocyclotron. The regenerator field (shaded zone) fixes the nodes and brings about radial oscillations of increasing amplitude. The rosette trajectory resulting from betatron oscillations around an inner equilibrium orbit is also shown. The numbers label successive regenerated orbits.

unperturbed field. This is just what is needed to correct for the precession of the nodes, provided that the regenerator field has the proper strength. On the other hand, fixing the nodes brings about an increasing amplitude of oscillation in each turn, (cf. Fig. 6.19) until the particles finally reach a magnetic channel and escape. The entire process may take 20 or 30 turns. Since its inception (Tuck and Teng, 1951 ; Le Couteur and Lipton, 1956) the method has been progressively refined, and extraction efficiencies as high as 10 per cent of the circulating beam have been reported (de Kruiff and Verster, 1961/1962).

    In proton synchrotrons there is one orbit for all energies. Any magnetic perturbation would interfere with the whole process of acceleration, which makes the regenerator method impractical. But the slowness of the acceleration cycle makes it possible to introduce a target in the acceleration chamber only when the protons are near their maximum energy. This is the basis of the most usual methods of beam extraction. As an example, the extraction arrangement of the ZGS is shown schematically in Fig. 6.17. Upon traversing the target the protons lose some energy and the radius of curvature of their path is consequently reduced. This enables the particles to enter a deflecting magnet (which they normally miss during acceleration) which deflects them out of the synchrotron. This system of targets and magnets can be duplicated so as to achieve two separate and simultaneous proton beams in two experimental areas.

CHAPTER 7

The Principle of Strong Focussing by Alternating Gradients

The synchrotrons described in Chapter 6 make possible the attainment, in theory at least, of any desired energy. The only limitation is of a financial kind, thus providing a spur for the search for more economical processes of acceleration. Money may be saved in several different ways: it may be sought to achieve a higher energy with the same investment, even at the cost of losing in beam intensity. This is the case of the proton synchrotron as compared with the synchrocyclotron. Or the aim may be to increase the beam intensity with no loss of energy. And of course, what is most desirable, greater energy and intensity may be pursued with no proportional increase in cost. The principle of strong focussing, with consequences perhaps as far reaching as those of the principle of phase stability, meets these needs.

The cost of a circular accelerator depends essentially on the size of the magnet. This is in turn roughly proportional to the volume in which the magnetic field must be established. The doughnut-shaped acceleration chamber of synchrotrons reduces this volume very much compared to that of synchrocyclotrons, but even so its size is ultimately determined by the cross-section of the beam which it must contain. The beam cross-section will obviously be smaller the stronger the radial and vertical focussing forces tend to confine the particles in the neighbourhood of the equilibrium orbit. The conclusion is therefore that the cost of an accelerator is strongly dependent on its focussing properties.

1. Alternating Gradient Systems

The accelerators studied in Chapters 5 and 6 achieved radial and vertical focussing by a compromise between two opposite requirements. A field rapidly decreasing with radius provides good vertical focussing, while radial focussing requires a field either increasing with radius or at least decreasing not faster than $1/r$. The compromise results from precisely this type of decrease.

As shown in Chapter 5, both vertical and radial oscillations are bounded if the field index n falls in the range $0 < n < 1$. If $n < 0$ (field increasing with radius) there is only radial focussing, whilst $n > 1$ provides only vertical focussing. In 1949 a Greek engineer, Christophilos, suggested building a machine based on a compromise different from that represented by the condition $0 < n < 1$. He thought in terms of a circular accelerator made up of sectors in which the field alternatively increases and decreases with radius, while having the same value in all sectors at the radius of the synchronous orbit. Christophilos' work remained unknown to the scientific world, to the extent that three years later Courant, Livingston and Snyder, being unaware of it, made a similar proposal and arrived at the conclusion that it was perfectly sound. On the other hand it was soon recognized that this principle of strong focussing, or alternating gradient, as it is also called, is nothing but the application to accelerators of more general laws governing the stability of mechanical, optical and electrical systems. It is well known, for instance, that a system formed of a convergent and a divergent lens can be totally convergent. A beam of particles is similar to a pencil of light, for which the sector with $n > 1$ behaves as a convergent lens in the vertical direction and as a divergent lens in the horizontal plane (Fig. 7.1). The converse will be true for a sector with

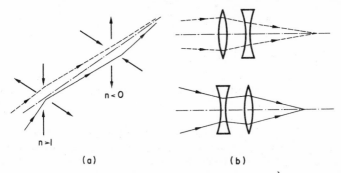

Fig. 7.1. Forces acting on particles in an alternating gradient system. (*a*) Over-all focussing effect of two alternating sectors on particles moving on a vertical plane (dashed line) and on a horizontal plane (full line). (*b*) Optical analogue of both sectors for each plane.

negative *n*, namely it will be convergent in the horizontal plane and divergent in the vertical plane. In this way there is a succession of convergent and divergent lenses in both planes, thus providing the necessary vertical and radial focussing.

2. Quadrupolar Lenses

The principle of strong focussing had an immediate application to the construction of linear accelerators. The requirement of phase stability in these machines leads to electrostatic defocussing of the beam by drift tubes.

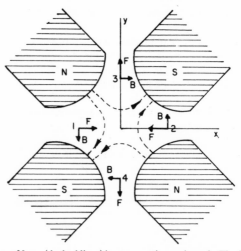

Fig. 7.2. Lines of force (dashed lines) in a magnetic quadrupole. The forces acting on positively charged particles coming from behind the paper towards the reader are shown as *F*.

The use of metallic grids to modify the shape of the lines of force brings about, as remarked in Chapter 4, the loss of an important fraction of the beam hitting the grids. The alternating gradient lenses solved the problem of achieving focussing with no loss of beam. These lenses consist of magnetic quadrupoles as shown in Fig. 7.2. The magnetic field produced by the four polar tips is zero at the centre, whilst the lines of force in other regions look like those of Fig. 7.2. Let us consider positive particles coming from behind the paper towards the reader: the course of those going through the centre is not altered, but those passing through points such as 1 and 2 suffer the action of forces directed towards the centre (focussing effect), whereas the forces applied to particles in points 3 and 4 are directed away from the centre (defocussing effect).

The optical analogue of the magnetic quadrupole described above is a lens convergent in the horizontal plane and divergent in the vertical plane. If following this first quadrupole there is a second one, similar in all respects but rotated 90°, namely divergent in the horizontal plane and convergent in the vertical plane, the system will behave like a succession of divergent and convergent lenses in both planes, thus ensuring, if properly arranged, a net focussing effect. The resulting trajectories are shown in Fig. 7.3. When used to provide focussing for linear accelerators the quadrupoles are mounted inside the drift tubes.

Let us now proceed to a more quantitative treatment of the strong focussing lenses. The polar tips usually have the shape of equilateral

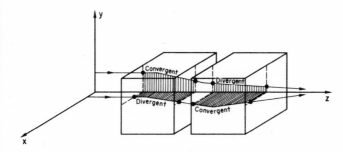

Fig. 7.3. Trajectories of particles traversing a quadrupolar lens. (After Courant *et al.*, 1952).

hyperbolae. If saturation effects in the iron are not important, it can then be shown that the lines of force are also hyperbolic and that the magnetic field components have equations

$$B_x = ky, \qquad B_y = kx, \qquad (7.1)$$

where k is a constant, equal to the gradient of the field. Referring to Fig. 7.2, where the particles are assumed to move along the z-axis with velocity v, the force acting on a particle at the point (x, y) has components

$$F_x = -qvB_y = -qvkx , \qquad F_y = qvB_x = qvky . \tag{7.2}$$

The equations of motion can be written down at once. They are

$$m\ddot{x} = -qvkx , \qquad m\ddot{y} = qvky , \tag{7.3}$$

where the dots denote differentiation with respect to time. This can be changed into differentiation with respect to z through the substitution $\mathrm{d}z = v\,\mathrm{d}t$, giving

$$x'' + \omega^2 x = 0 \qquad y'' - \omega^2 y = 0 , \tag{7.4}$$

where the derivatives with respect to z are indicated by primes and $\omega^2 = qk/(mv)$. We have implicitly assumed that k is positive (quadrupole focussing in the x-direction, defocussing in the y-direction). If $k < 0$, the equation for x is changed into that for y and vice versa. The solutions of these equations are well known: they are linear combinations of sines and cosines in the first and hyperbolic sines and cosines in the second equation. The coefficients in those combinations depend on the initial values of the displacements and their derivatives. One obtains

$$\begin{aligned} x &= x_0 \cos \omega z + x_0' \omega^{-1} \sin \omega z \\ x' &= -x_0 \omega \sin \omega z + x_0' \cos \omega z \end{aligned} \tag{7.5}$$

in the focussing plane and

$$\begin{aligned} y &= y_0 \cosh \omega z + y_0' \omega^{-1} \sinh \omega z \\ y' &= y_0 \omega \sinh \omega z + y_0' \cosh \omega z \end{aligned} \tag{7.6}$$

in the defocussing plane. The subscript zero indicates values at the origin of the coordinates. The systems of eqns. (7.5) and (7.6) are equivalent to the matrix equations

$$\begin{pmatrix} x \\ x' \end{pmatrix} = \mathbf{F} \begin{pmatrix} x_0 \\ x_0' \end{pmatrix} = \begin{pmatrix} \cos \omega z & \dfrac{1}{\omega} \sin \omega z \\ -\omega \sin \omega z & \cos \omega z \end{pmatrix} \begin{pmatrix} x_0 \\ x_0' \end{pmatrix} \tag{7.5A}$$

and

$$\begin{pmatrix} y \\ y' \end{pmatrix} = \mathbf{D} \begin{pmatrix} y_0 \\ y_0' \end{pmatrix} = \begin{pmatrix} \cosh \omega z & \dfrac{1}{\omega} \sinh \omega z \\ \omega \sinh \omega z & \cosh \omega z \end{pmatrix} \begin{pmatrix} y_0 \\ y_0' \end{pmatrix} \tag{7.6A}$$

Similarly, as the reader may verify, the matrix

$$\mathbf{O} = \begin{pmatrix} 1 & s \\ 0 & 1 \end{pmatrix} \tag{7.7}$$

corresponds to the solution of the equation $x'' = 0$, representing the motion in a field-free region of length s. In this way, matrices can be used to study the motion of the particles as they proceed along regions with different magnetic fields, provided that their coordinates satisfy equations of the type (7.4). A sequence of such regions is represented by the product of the corresponding matrices. A strong focussing lens, formed by two quadrupoles of length L separated by a distance s has the matrix

$$\mathbf{M} = \mathbf{DOF} = \begin{pmatrix} \cosh \omega L & \dfrac{1}{\omega} \sinh \omega L \\ \omega \sinh \omega L & \cosh \omega L \end{pmatrix} \begin{pmatrix} 1 & s \\ 0 & 1 \end{pmatrix} \begin{pmatrix} \cos \omega L & \dfrac{1}{\omega} \sin \omega L \\ -\omega \sin \omega L & \cos \omega L \end{pmatrix} \tag{7.8}$$

for the motion in one plane (for example, the x-z plane) and

$$\mathbf{N} = \mathbf{FOD} \tag{7.9}$$

in the other. The optical properties of the lens depend on the matrix elements M_{ij} and N_{ij}. For example, let us obtain the position of the focal point in the *DOF* plane. This is, by definition, the point where an outgoing ray crosses the axis ($x = 0$) if it has originally entered the lens parallel to the axis ($x'_0 = 0$). The focus will be located at a distance d from the exit face of the lens such that

$$\begin{pmatrix} 0 \\ x' \end{pmatrix} = \begin{pmatrix} 1 & d \\ 0 & 1 \end{pmatrix} \begin{pmatrix} M_{11} & M_{12} \\ M_{21} & M_{22} \end{pmatrix} \begin{pmatrix} x_0 \\ 0 \end{pmatrix}.$$

A calculation of the matrix elements yields

$$0 = M_{11} + d M_{21}$$
$$x' = M_{21} x_0 ,$$

which allow the calculation of $d = -M_{11}/M_{21}$ and of the focal distance $f = -1/M_{21}$. Matrix algebra of this type is fundamental for obtaining criteria of stability in all strong focussing machines.

3. Betatron Oscillations in Strong Focussing Machines

Shortly after the proposal of alternating gradient focussing had been published, several laboratories started studies for the building of machines, particularly synchrotrons, based on the new principle. Analogous to the classical weak-focussing synchrotrons, their magnetic fields were to vary with time, the radio frequency being kept constant for electrons and variable for protons. The polar tips, however, were to be shaped as shown in Fig. 7.4, providing more intense fields in the regions where they are closer together.

The first projects were in fact quite appealing. Livingston, Courant and

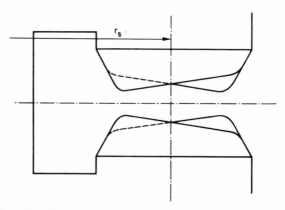

Fig. 7.4. Profile of the polar tips in a strong focussing synchrotron. The dashed line shows the profile of the next pole pieces.

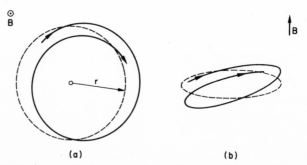

Fig. 7.5. Betatron oscillations around an equilibrium orbit in a weak focussing machine. (*a*) Radial oscillation. (*b*) Vertical oscillation.

Snyder, for instance, suggested the construction of a 30-GeV proton synchrotron, with field gradients of 4 000 gauss per centimetre. The beam would be contained in a doughnut-shaped acceleration chamber with a cross-section of only 3 cm diameter. A conventional weak-focussing accelerator of the same energy would require an acceleration chamber with rectangular cross-section of 1.5 m $\times$ 6 m to accommodate the beam!

It was soon realised, however, that these initial estimates were rather too optimistic (Adams, Hine and Lawson, 1953). To understand why, we have to recall the discussion on betatron oscillations analysed in Chapter 5. It was then seen that the actual path of a particle (and this applies to any circular accelerator) consists of an oscillation about the ideal equilibrium orbit. The frequencies of both radial and vertical oscillations in weak-focussing machines, subject to the condition that $0 < n < 1$, are always smaller than the rotation frequency of the particle (see eqns. (5.20) and (5.21)). That is to say, the angle between two successive crossings of the equilibrium orbit is always greater than $180°$, as shown in Fig. 7.5. On the other hand, the strong focussing forces associated with alternating gradients induce rapid oscillations about the equilibrium orbit, resulting in trajectories resembling those of Fig. 7.6. In short, strong focussing forces bring about several oscillations per turn, the number of which increases with stronger gradients, whereas weak focussing forces always result in less than one oscillation per turn. Now, in the actual construction of a machine there are slight deviations of the field from the theoretical values

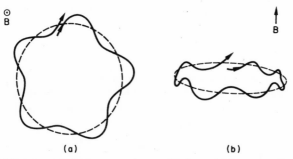

Fig. 7.6. Betatron oscillations around an equilibrium orbit in a strong focussing machine. (*a*) Radial oscillation. (*b*) Vertical oscillation.

which cannot be avoided. If there were an integral number of oscillations per turn the particles would perform exactly the same trajectory in each turn, periodically suffering the same perturbation wherever these imperfections might be present. This would result in forced oscillations of increasing amplitude, leading to the loss of the beam against the walls of the chamber. Even if the number of oscillations is not an integer, but large enough, the trajectories in subsequent turns may be sufficiently close together to bring about the same effect. This was the case in the project mentioned above, in which there would be about 50 oscillations per turn. An error of 0·2 mm in the alignment of a magnetic sector (it is worth bearing in mind that this machine would have a radius of 100 metres) would suffice to make the beam disappear after ten turns. The analysis of betatron oscillations can be conducted with the help of the matrix algebra developed in the last paragraph. Let us note that in each magnet section the equation for small radial oscillations (5.19), derived for the cyclotron, is still applicable. We shall find it convenient to use as independent variable the length s along the equilibrium orbit. Since $ds = v\,dt = \omega_0 r_0\,dt$, (5.19) is transformed into

$$\frac{d^2 \rho}{ds^2} + (1-n)\frac{\rho}{r_0^2} = 0. \tag{7.10}$$

But from the definition (5.7) of the field index n:

$$\frac{n}{r_0^2} = -\frac{1}{B_0 r_0}\frac{dB}{dr} = -\frac{q}{p}\frac{dB}{dr} = -\omega^2$$

where ω^2 is the quantity defined in connexion with quadrupolar lenses in the last paragraph. We finally obtain

$$\frac{d^2 \rho}{ds^2} + \left(1 - \frac{1}{n}\right)\omega^2 \rho = 0. \tag{7.11}$$

In strong focussing machines n is of the order of 200 or more. The term $1/n$ can be neglected in eqn. (7.11). On the other hand, since the field gradient and therefore ω^2 alternate in sign in different sectors, we finally obtain

$$\frac{d^2 \rho}{ds^2} \pm \omega^2 \rho = 0 \tag{7.12}$$

where the plus sign corresponds to focussing sectors and the minus sign to defocussing sectors. The reader may verify that the equation (5.11) for vertical motion leads to a similar result. The equations (7.12) are formally identical to (7.4). Therefore the focussing properties of the accelerator are the same as those of a sequence of alternating quadrupole magnets.

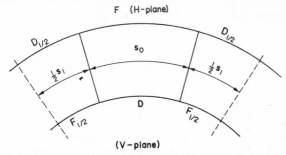

Fig. 7.7. Basic cell used to describe radial and vertical motions in an alternating gradient machine. If the sequence $D_{\frac{1}{2}} F D_{\frac{1}{2}}$ is adopted for one plane, the resulting sequence for the other plane is $F_{\frac{1}{2}} D F_{\frac{1}{2}}$.

The matrix formalism can be applied to a 'basic cell' in the accelerator, shown in Fig. 7.7. It consists of half a defocussing sector (length $\frac{1}{2}s_1$), a whole focussing sector (length s_0) and half a defocussing sector (length $\frac{1}{2}s_1$). Since this configuration repeats itself indefinitely along a closed orbit, it is clear that the stability of the orbit depends only on the behaviour of the basic cell. The matrix corresponding to the basic cell will be the product

$$\mathbf{H} = \mathbf{D}_{\frac{1}{2}} \cdot \mathbf{F} \cdot \mathbf{D}_{\frac{1}{2}} = \begin{pmatrix} \cosh \omega \dfrac{s_1}{2} & \dfrac{1}{\omega} \sinh \omega \dfrac{s_1}{2} \\ \omega \sinh \omega \dfrac{s_1}{2} & \cosh \omega \dfrac{s_1}{2} \end{pmatrix} \begin{pmatrix} \cos \omega s_0 & \dfrac{1}{\omega} \sin \omega s_0 \\ -\omega \sin \omega s_0 & \cos \omega s_0 \end{pmatrix}$$

$$\times \begin{pmatrix} \cosh \omega \dfrac{s_1}{2} & \dfrac{1}{\omega} \sinh \omega \dfrac{s_1}{2} \\ \omega \sinh \omega \dfrac{s_1}{2} & \cosh \omega \dfrac{s_1}{2} \end{pmatrix}. \tag{7.13}$$

While this is true for one plane, the horizontal plane for example, the focussing properties of the basic cell will be reversed for the other plane; in other words, the corresponding matrix for the vertical plane will be

$$
\mathbf{V} = \mathbf{F}_{\frac{1}{2}} . \mathbf{D} . \mathbf{F}_{\frac{1}{2}} =
\begin{pmatrix}
\cos \omega \dfrac{s_1}{2} & \dfrac{1}{\omega} \sin \omega \dfrac{s_1}{1} \\[2ex]
-\omega \sin \omega \dfrac{s_1}{2} & \cos \omega \dfrac{s_1}{2}
\end{pmatrix}
\begin{pmatrix}
\cosh \omega s_0 & \dfrac{1}{\omega} \sinh \omega s_0 \\[2ex]
\omega \sinh \omega s_0 & \cosh \omega s_0
\end{pmatrix}
$$

$$
\times
\begin{pmatrix}
\cos \omega \dfrac{s_1}{2} & \dfrac{1}{\omega} \sin \omega \dfrac{s_1}{2} \\[2ex]
-\omega \sin \omega \dfrac{s_1}{2} & \cos \omega \dfrac{s_1}{2}
\end{pmatrix}.
\tag{7.14}
$$

We may now ask what condition should be fulfilled by the product matrices $\mathbf{H}$ and $\mathbf{V}$ to ensure both radial and vertical focussing. The answer is that they must be of the $\mathbf{F}$-type, as in eqn. (7.5^{A}), that is, they must have cosines as diagonal elements. In fact, performing the matrix product indicated in (7.13) one can write formally

$$
\mathbf{H} =
\begin{pmatrix}
\cos \mu_{\mathrm{H}} & \dfrac{1}{K_{\mathrm{H}}} \sin \mu_{\mathrm{H}} \\[2ex]
-K_{\mathrm{H}} \sin \mu_{\mathrm{H}} & \cos \mu_{\mathrm{H}}
\end{pmatrix}.
$$

A similar expression can be obtained for $\mathbf{V}$, with

$$
\cos \mu_{\mathrm{H}} = \cosh \omega s_1 \cos \omega s_0
\tag{7.15}
$$

in the $\mathbf{D}_{\frac{1}{2}} . \mathbf{F} . \mathbf{D}_{\frac{1}{2}}$ plane and

$$
\cos \mu_{\mathrm{V}} = \cos \omega s_1 \cosh \omega s_0
\tag{7.16}
$$

in the $\mathbf{F}_{\frac{1}{2}} . \mathbf{D} . \mathbf{F}_{\frac{1}{2}}$ plane. The parameters K_{H} and K_{V} are complicated combinations of hyperbolic and trigonometric functions. The whole procedure is justified only if

$$
-1 < \cos \mu_{\mathrm{H}} < 1 ,
\tag{7.17}
$$

$$
-1 < \cos \mu_{\mathrm{V}} < 1 ,
\tag{7.18}
$$

with $\cos \mu_{\mathrm{H}}, \cos \mu_{\mathrm{V}}$ defined by eqns. (7.15) and (7.16). These are the required conditions of stability. Another variation can be introduced, namely, different values of ω, which we shall denote by ω_0 and ω_1, in different sectors. If such is the case (7.15) and (7.16) must be replaced by

$$\cos \mu_H = \cosh \omega_1 s_1 \cos \omega_0 s_0 + \tfrac{1}{2} \left(\frac{\omega_1}{\omega_0} - \frac{\omega_0}{\omega_1} \right) \sin \omega_0 s_0 \sinh \omega_1 s_1 \quad (7.19)$$

$$\cos \mu_V = \cos \omega_1 s_1 \cosh \omega_0 s_0 + \tfrac{1}{2} \left(\frac{\omega_0}{\omega_1} - \frac{\omega_1}{\omega_0} \right) \sinh \omega_0 s_0 \sin \omega_1 s_1 \quad (7.20)$$

but the conditions of stability (7.17) and (7.18) are still valid. Fig. 7.8 shows how these conditions define a region in the $(\omega_0 s_0, \omega_1 s_1)$-plane, within

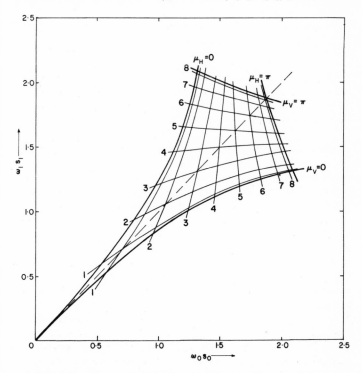

Fig. 7.8. Stability limits and resonance lines in an A. G. synchrotron. The diagram has been drawn for a number of basic cells $N = 18$. The resonance lines are numbered according to the values of l in eqn. (7.21).

which the working point of the accelerator must be chosen. The network of lines inside the stable region corresponds to the 'stop bands' or integral resonances which must also be avoided. These lines are the loci of points where the number of betatron oscillations per turn is an integer.

The position of the resonance lines can be established by noticing that μ_H and μ_V are the phase shifts of the betatron oscillations in a basic cell (for example, if $\mu_H = \pi$, ρ is changed into $-\rho$). If the accelerator has N basic cells the change of phase per turn will be $N\mu$ (we drop the subscripts in this discussion), and the number of oscillations per turn will be

$$Q = \frac{N\mu}{2\pi}.$$

The condition for a resonance is therefore that $Q = l$, an integer, or

$$\mu = 2l\pi/N . \tag{7.21}$$

Since the maximum value of μ in the stability region is π (cos $\mu = -1$), l is restricted to the values $l = 1, 2, ..., \frac{1}{2}N$. The equations for the resonance lines are obtained by replacement of (7.21) in (7.19) and (7.20) with those values of l.

The stable operation of the machine is restricted to working points inside any of the deformed squares in Fig. 7.8, limited by resonance lines. As the number of sectors increases so does the number of resonance lines ($= \frac{1}{2}N$) and the area of each square becomes smaller. This is an undesirable feature, since some changes in the working point must be expected during the magnetic cycle, as saturation effects appear. Moreover, the working point should not cross the half-integral $(Q = l + \frac{1}{2})$ resonance line too slowly. An integral number of oscillations is performed in two revolutions of the particle in such a case. Typical values of Q in present-day strong focussing synchrotrons are 6·4 in the 6-GeV Cambridge Electron Accelerator, 6·25 in the CERN proton synchrotron and 8·75 in the Brookhaven machine.

The resonance effects outlined above only set a limit to the applications of the alternating gradient principle, but do not impair its use. In practice, the acceleration chamber of a strong focussing machine can be thirty times smaller than that of a conventional machine of the same energy. One should not think, however, that weak focussing synchrotrons have been definitely superseded. They still have advantages in the 3-10 GeV range. In fact, their larger acceleration chambers provide more acceptance (range of coordinates and momenta of the particles that can be accepted for successful acceleration) at injection than the strong focussing machines. Therefore they are able to yield, with proper care in design, a higher beam intensity in that energy range. On the other hand, an alternating gradient accelerator has a greater acceptance at very high energies, which makes it definitely more convenient above, say, 15 GeV.

4. Phase Stability and Transition Energy in A.G. Synchrotrons

The mechanism of phase stability is also somewhat different in alternating gradient machines. Let us first recall the common features. A particle with a non-synchronous phase gains more (or less) energy than a synchronous particle when crossing the accelerating station. The period of revolution becomes correspondingly different, resulting in a change of phase at the next crossing of the station. The synchronous phase is the only stable one, and non-synchronous particles are either lost or caught into the phase stability mechanism, their phases becoming closer to the synchronous phase during acceleration. In a conventional synchrotron a particle will move on a circular orbit whatever its energy, the changes in the period of revolution being brought about by the variation of the field with radius and the relativistic change of mass with energy, as discussed in Chapter 6. But the only circular orbit in an alternating gradient machine is that of the synchronous particle, where the field is everywhere the same. Non-synchronous particles of higher or lower energy than the synchronous particle are subjected to different fields in different magnetic sectors and the radii of curvature of their paths vary accordingly. The resulting trajectories look like those of Fig. 7.9, consisting of oscillations superimposed on a circumference which in turn corresponds to the *average* radial position of the particle. It must be borne in mind that these have nothing to do with the betatron oscillations discussed above, which are oscillations about equilibrium orbits. The undulating trajectories of non-synchronous particles are equilibrium orbits themselves.

Let us now assume that the magnetic sectors have field gradients equal in magnitude but of different sign. The field excess acting on the average circumference in one sector compensates the field defect in the next (notice the directions of increasing fields in Fig. 7.9), which would seem to imply that the net effect of the field is the same as that on the synchronous orbit. But the 'wiggles' in the orbit are such that the particle of higher energy, say, moves farther away from the synchronous orbit in sectors where the field

Particle Acceleration

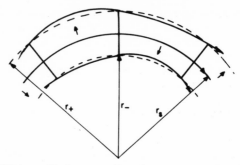

Fig. 7.9. Equilibrium orbits in a strong focussing synchrotron. The synchronous orbit is a circle of radius r_s, while r_+ and r_- are average radii for the orbits of particles with higher and lower energy than the synchronous energy, respectively. The arrows indicate directions of field increase.

increases with radius and comes closer to it where the field decreases with radius. The particle is then subject to a stronger field than that corresponding to its average radial displacement. The strong focussing system is more efficient, as it were, in making use of the field variations than the conventional arrangement. A small average radial displacement allows for relatively large variations of energy.

The length of the orbit is affected in a similar way. The relative increase in length dL/L and the relative increase in momentum dp/p are proportional in first approximation:

$$\frac{dL}{L} = \alpha \frac{dp}{p}. \tag{7.22}$$

The coefficient α is called the 'momentum compaction factor'. In a conventional machine $\alpha = 1/(1-n)$. As generally $n = 0.6$, $\alpha = 2.5$. On the other hand, the momentum compaction factor in an alternating gradient machine may be very small because of the effect described above, of the order of 0.01, for instance. The small value of α affects in turn the mechanism of phase stability. In fact, this mechanism depends essentially on the variation of the period of revolution with energy or momentum. The relative change of period results from its general definition: $\tau = L/v$ as

$$\frac{d\tau}{\tau} = \frac{dL}{L} - \frac{dv}{v}.$$

On the other hand, the relative change in velocity is, according to relativistic dynamics:

$$\frac{dv}{v} = \left(\frac{W_0}{W}\right)^2 \frac{dp}{p}.$$

The relative variation of the period is then:

$$\frac{d\tau}{\tau} = \left[\alpha - \left(\frac{W_0}{W}\right)^2\right] \frac{dp}{p}. \tag{7.23}$$

The requirement in a weak focussing field that $n < 1$ implies that $\alpha > 1$, and the quantity in square brackets above will always be positive. The increase in the length of the orbit overcomes that in the velocity, and the period of revolution will increase with momentum. This is what happens in the synchrocyclotron, and we have already seen (Chapter 6) that in such a case there exists a synchronous phase in that part of the voltage wave *decreasing* with time.

The low value of the momentum compaction factor in strong focussing machines ($\alpha \ll 1$) implies that at the beginning of the acceleration, when the kinetic energy is small compared with the rest energy and consequently W_0/W is of the order of 1, the quantity in square brackets in (7.23) is negative. The relative increase in velocity is more important than the increase in length of the orbit, that is to say, the period of revolution *decreases* with increasing momentum. Similar conditions are met in the linear accelerator, where the fastest particles spend the shortest times in travelling the distance between two successive accelerating gaps. But in that case the equilibrium phase, as was seen in Chapter 4, corresponds to the portion of the voltage wave *increasing* with time. In the course of acceleration, the particles may reach the so called transition energy,

$$W_t = W_0/\sqrt{\alpha} \tag{7.24}$$

at which the period of revolution stops decreasing and starts increasing with energy. There are then two opposite mechanisms of phase stability in a strong focussing synchrotron: one is analogous to that operating in a linear accelerator and is related to the increase in the particle's velocity; the other, characteristic of the synchrotron, is connected with the increase in orbit length. The transition energy marks the instant at which the former type of synchronism is replaced by the latter. When this energy is reached, the particles are already grouped around the synchronous phase in the increasing part of the voltage wave, which is precisely the unstable portion in the synchrotron-type acceleration that follows. Unless there is a sudden and carefully timed shift in the radio-frequency wave such that the particles meet a decreasing voltage at the next crossing of the accelerating station, they will not be caught into the phase stability process and will be lost after reaching the transition energy. A value of 0·01 for the compaction factor yields a transition energy $W_t = 10 W_0$, which corresponds to a kinetic energy of 8·34 GeV in the case of protons.

It is not beyond the means of modern technology to produce the 'change of step' in the frequency needed to exceed the transition energy. In fact this method has been used successfully in the first two alternating gradient synchrotrons to operate: the 28-GeV machine installed at Geneva by the CERN (initials of Centre Européen de Recherche Nucléaire) and the Brookhaven 32-GeV synchrotron in the United States.

There is still another way of overcoming the difficulties associated with the transition energy, namely forcing its value far up to infinity by making the compaction factor equal to zero. This of course implies major changes in design, like those present in a 7-GeV machine built as a model for a larger (70-GeV) one ordered by the Soviet Academy of Science (Vladimirskii and Tarasov, 1956). The magnetic ring in this machine consists of 56 periods of two magnets each, one producing vertical focussing, the other horizontal focussing. One out of four horizontal focussing magnets

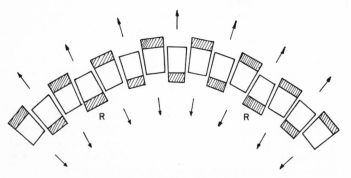

Fig. 7.10. Structure of a synchrotron with compensating units. The magnets with reversed field are marked as *R*. The arrows indicate the direction of the field gradient.

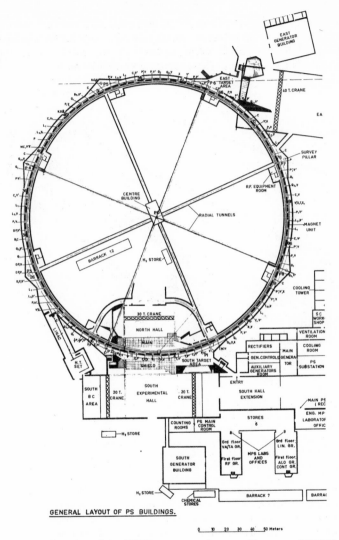

GENERAL LAYOUT OF PS BUILDINGS.

0 10 20 30 40 50 Meters

Fig. 7.11. Plan view of the CERN proton synchrotron. (*Courtesy of CERN*).

is a compensating unit, in which the magnetic field is reversed and the trajectories have the 'wrong' curvature. Particles of different energies have orbits of the same length, which amounts to saying that the momentum compaction factor is zero. The machine has 98 ordinary magnets, in which

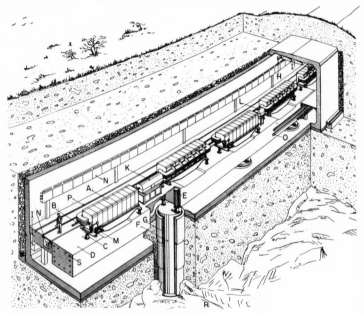

Fig. 7.12. Sectional drawing of the CERN proton synchrotron. A, magnet; B, vacuum chamber; C, screw jack; D, concrete ring; E, elastic supports; F, concrete column based on rock; G, bitumen; H, 2 tons crane; I, ventilation; K, R. F. cavity; L, magnetic lens; M, vacuum pump; N, electric cables; O, magnet water cooling; P, rails; Q, earth; R, rock; S, temperature regulating water pipes. (*Courtesy of CERN*).

the radius of curvature of the synchronous orbit is 27·8 m, and 14 compensating magnets with radius of curvature −53·5 m (Fig. 7.10). The vacuum chamber has a cross-section of 8 cm × 11 cm. There are 12·75 betatron oscillations per turn. The disadvantage of this type of machine lies in its being about 25 per cent longer than a synchrotron with no compensating units, and correspondingly more costly. In practice, however, there must be some compensation because of a simpler radio-frequency generator.

The CERN and Brookhaven machines are very similar in construction. Views of the CERN synchrotron can be seen in Figs. 7.11 and 7.12. Its radius is 100 m, whereas that of the Brookhaven machine is 128·5 m. The advantages of the alternating gradient system can be best described by what is called vertical or radial relative aperture. This is the ratio between the height or width of the acceleration chamber, respectively, and the orbit radius. Typical values of the vertical relative aperture in weak focussing synchrotrons range between 0·01 and 0·02, and those of the radial aperture between 0·04 and 0·08. On the other hand, the Brookhaven machine has apertures 0·0008 (vertical) and 0·0014 (radial) and the CERN synchrotron has the same value 0·0018 for both apertures. The magnets in these machines are arranged in groups called periods and superperiods.

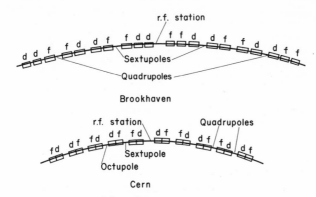

Fig. 7.13. Superperiods in the CERN and Brookhaven machines. The magnets are labelled *F* or *D* depending on their effect on radial oscillations.

The former are pairs of focussing and defocussing magnets, while the latter are groups of magnets separated by straight sections (Fig. 7.13). There are ten superperiods at Geneva and twelve at Brookhaven.

In other respects there are no big differences between weak and strong focussing machines. In both cases the particles are pre-accelerated before injection, although the higher final energy of alternating gradient synchrotrons requires a higher injection energy. In both the CERN and Brookhaven machines the injection energy is 50 MeV, obtained with a linear accelerator. Characteristic data of these machines are given in Table 7.1.

It is worth while pointing out that the first Brookhaven alternating gradient synchrotron was in fact a 'sham' 10-MeV electron accelerator in which the magnetic guiding fields were simulated by electrostatic fields. It was possible to show experimentally on this machine that the problems associated with the transition energy were actually solvable, thus paving the way to the construction of the real proton synchrotron.

TABLE 7.1
Design data of CERN and Brookhaven synchrotrons

	CERN	Brookhaven
Maximum energy (GeV)	28	32
Field at maximum energy (kilogauss)	14	13
Injection field (gauss)	147	121
Injection energy (MeV)	50	50
Orbit radius (m)	100	128·5
Betatron oscillations per turn	6·25	8·75
Field index	288	357
Synchronous phase	30°	30°
Accelerating stations	16	12
Initial frequency	2·9	1·4
Final frequency	9·5	4·5

5. A.G. Electron Synchrotrons

The application of the alternating gradient principle to electron synchrotrons has been much more straightforward. The transition energy is of the order of 5 MeV, which can be easily reached with a Van de Graaff generator or linear accelerator used to accelerate the electrons before injection. The whole process of acceleration inside the synchrotron is then performed above the transition energy. The savings which can be made through the application of the strong focussing system are illustrated by the fact that the iron in the magnet of the 1·5-GeV synchrotron at Cornell University, in the United States, weighs only 20 tons (Fig. 7.14). The same university has a 300-MeV conventional electron synchrotron in which the

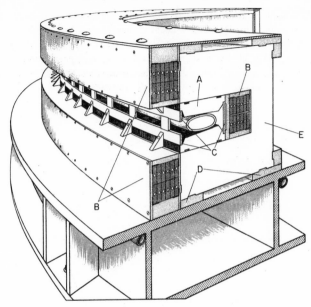

Fig. 7.14. One quadrant of the Cornell 1·5-GeV electron synchrotron. The orbit radius is 3·81 m. A, pole piece; B, coils; C, pole piece spacers; D, rails; E, magnet yoke. (*By courtesy of Dr. R. R. Wilson*)

iron weighs 80 tons. A limit is set to the energy attainable with these machines because of radiation losses, ever present in the case of electrons. The electron synchrotron of highest energy (6 GeV) is the Cambridge Electron Accelerator, belonging to Harvard University in the U.S.A. Other machines of similar design are nearing completion at Hamburg, Germany and at Erevan, Armenia, U.S.S.R.

In the Cambridge Accelerator a rather low peak field of 7 600 gauss has been chosen, to allow operation at a large radius (35·4 m) and therefore minimize the radiation losses (cf. eqn. (6.18)). Even so, the radiation loss per turn is 4·5 MeV at the maximum energy of 6 GeV. A tenfold variation of the accelerating voltage is required to compensate the varying radiation losses during the acceleration cycle. The electrons are injected at 25 MeV, well above the transition energy, by means of a linear accelerator. The injection energy in the 10-GeV electron synchrotron at Cornell is even higher, 200 MeV (150 MeV with full load). The orbit radius is 100 m, the magnetic field at 10 GeV being only 3·3 kG. Even so, the radiation loss per turn amounts to 10·4 MeV, which must be supplied by four waveguide accelerators located in straight sections of the machine.

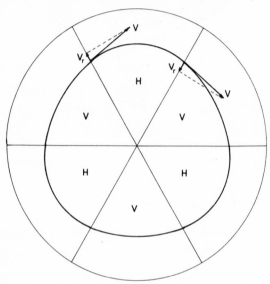

Fig. 7.15. Path of a particle in an azimuthally varying field cyclotron. The radial components of velocity, v_r are shown at the boundaries between hills (denoted as H) and valleys (denoted as V).

6. Azimuthally varying Field Cyclotrons

The first proposal for the application of alternating gradients to a cyclotron came long before the formulation of the principle of strong focussing itself. It is due to Thomas (1938), whose paper passed practically unheeded by the scientific world at that time. The merits of Thomas's suggestion have now been recognized, and several machines based on his ideas are operating successfully.

The radial decrease of magnetic field required to maintain vertical stability in the conventional cyclotron brings about a loss of synchronism between the particle and the radio-frequency field at energies of about 25 MeV. This difficulty was circumvented by frequency modulation in the synchrocyclotron, but at the cost of a hundredfold reduction in beam intensity. Thomas proposed to add triangular iron slabs to the pole tips of a cyclotron magnet, so as to reduce the gap and increase the field in certain sectors (called hills) alternating with sectors of lower field (called valleys). The path of a particle in such a field is no longer a circle, but a sort of curved polygon as shown in Fig. 7.15, with a more pronounced curvature in hills than in valleys. This orbit does not cross the boundaries between hills and valleys at right angles. The particle, therefore, has a non-zero radial component of velocity v_r. On the other hand, the fringe fields between valleys and hills have non-zero azimuthal components B_θ above and below the median plane (cf. Fig. 7.16). The interaction between v_r and

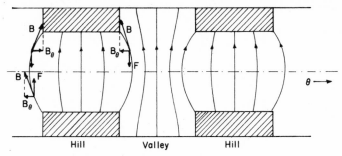

Fig. 7.16. Lines of force in the fringe fields between hills and valleys. The azimuthal component of the field above and below the median plane, B_θ, and the radial velocity v_r shown in Fig. 7.15, produce the focussing force F.

B_θ provides a vertical focussing force F_z for particles outside the median plane. If this force suffices to produce vertical stability one can shape the *average* field on the orbit so that it increases with radius and provides radial focussing as well as synchronism with a constant radio frequency applied to the dees. The condition for synchronism is

$$\langle \omega \rangle = \frac{v}{\langle r \rangle} = \frac{q\langle B \rangle}{m} = \frac{q\langle B \rangle}{m_0}(1 - \beta^2)^{\frac{1}{2}} = \frac{qB_0}{m_0} = \text{const}, \quad (7.25)$$

where the symbols $\langle \ \rangle$ denote averages taken on the orbit and the subscript

o refers to values at the centre of the machine. The law of variation of the average field is obtained as

$$\langle B \rangle = B_o \left[1 - \left(\frac{\omega \langle r \rangle}{c} \right)^2 \right]^{-\frac{1}{2}}. \tag{7.26}$$

It is customary to define the field index in these machines as

$$k = \frac{\langle r \rangle}{\langle B \rangle} \frac{\mathrm{d}\langle B \rangle}{\mathrm{d}\langle r \rangle}, \tag{7.27}$$

which, together with eqn. (7.26) gives

$$k = \frac{1}{(c/\omega \langle r \rangle)^2 - 1} = \frac{\beta^2}{1 - \beta^2}. \tag{7.28}$$

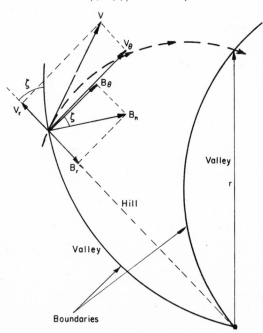

Fig. 7.17. Reinforcement of the vertical focussing effect achieved through spiral sector geometry. The horizontal component of the fringe field above the median plane is shown as B_n. It is normal to the sector boundary.

An interesting feature of these machines is that their field index is not left to the designer's will, as is the case, within certain limits, of conventional cyclotrons, but is determined by the dynamics of the particle trough eqn. (7.28). Since k is positive, the average field introduces a vertical defocussing effect that must be compensated by the Thomas force described above. At a certain energy (about 20 MeV) the field index becomes large enough to overcome the focussing effect at the boundaries between hills and valleys. The radial sector cyclotron ceases to be effective. A way out of this difficulty has been provided by the proposal of spiral sectors (Symon *et al.*, 1956), which increases the vertical focussing by slanting the sector boundaries with respect to the orbit (Fig. 7.17). The effect is similar to that produced by the slanted pole pieces described in connexion with the ZGS in the last chapter. In addition to B_θ a radial component of the fringe field, B_r, is present at the boundaries. Its magnitude depends on the angle ζ between the spiralling boundary and a radial line. A supplementary focussing force is obtained through the interaction of B_r and v_0.

The analysis of betatron oscillations in AVF cyclotrons requires the use of modern electronic computers. An estimate of the number of oscillations per turn is given by

$$
\begin{aligned}
Q_r^2 &= 1 + k \\
Q_z^2 &= -k + F^2(\tan^2\zeta + \tfrac{1}{2}),
\end{aligned} \tag{7.29}
$$

where F, defined by

$$
F^2 = \frac{\langle B^2 \rangle - \langle B \rangle^2}{\langle B \rangle^2},
$$

is the 'flutter factor', measuring in a sense the amount of variation of the field in hills and valleys.

Since k varies with the energy, a fixed operating point cannot be chosen as in other strong focussing machines. It is found from (7.28) and (7.29) that $Q_r = W/W_0$, so that a half-integral resonance occurs for protons at about 470 MeV ($Q_r = 1.5$). It seems that it is possible to cross this resonance without losing much beam, but the integral resonance appearing when the kinetic energy is equal to the rest energy of the particle, ($Q_r = 2$) is generally accepted as marking the ultimate limit of AVF cyclotrons.

Forty-two isochronous cyclotrons (as they are also called) are in operation or approaching completion at present (1966). They are extremely versatile machines: changes in the operating values of the field and the

Particle Acceleration

radio frequency allow the acceleration of different particles to various energies. However, the necessity of preserving the shape of the field given by eqn. (7.26) dictates the use of trimming circular coils for a final adjustment at each energy. Furthermore, other coils, usually located in the valleys, are used to compensate saturation effects as the field is changed.

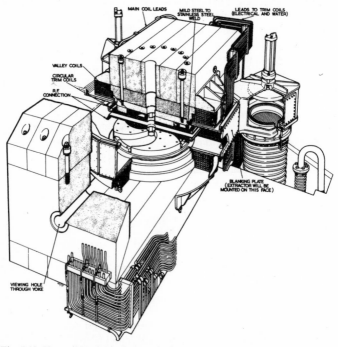

Fig. 7.18. Harwell Variable Energy Cyclotron magnet assembly. (*By courtesy of Dr. J. D. Lawson*).

A cut-away view of the magnet assembly in the Harwell Variable Energy Cyclotron is given in Fig. 7.18. The chart in Fig. 7.19 shows the energies and particles available in the ORIC (Oak Ridge Isochronous Cyclotron).

The beam extraction systems in these machines are similar to those used in conventional cyclotrons, based on electrostatic deflectors. Proper radial separation between orbits requires then a rather high (about 50 kV) accelerating voltage between dees. A regenerative method as used in some synchrocyclotrons would induce unwanted oscillations in the circulating beam. Furthermore, it lacks the flexibility required in a variable energy machine. These difficulties, however, have been successfully circumvented in the Birmingham radial sector cyclotron. Instead of a magnetic perturbation as in synchrocyclotrons, a properly shaped

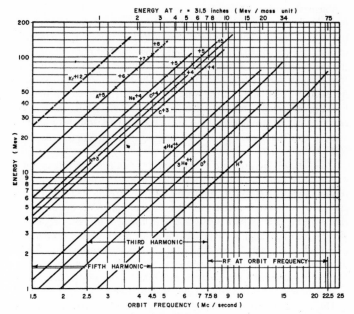

Fig. 7.19. Particles and energies obtainable from the Oak Ridge Isochronous Cyclotron.

electrostatic field induces radial oscillations resulting in the required separation between orbits. The strength of the electrostatic regenerator can in principle be easily varied according to the energy of the particles to be extracted. On the other hand, septum and deflector arrangements have been operated satisfactorily with proton energies of up to 50 MeV in the Berkeley 88-inch Cyclotron at the University of California. This is about the maximum energy available from these machines at present. Other AVF cyclotrons, known as 'meson factories' are still on the drawing board. They are planned to deliver high intensities (a few mA) of protons in the range of a few hundred MeV, capable of producing meson beams about a thousand times more intense than those available from existing synchrocyclotrons. Some of these machines are planned to accelerate negative instead of positive ions. This would make extraction problems far easier to solve. In fact, it suffices to convert the negative ions into positive ions by stripping off their electrons once they have reached the desired energy. This can be accomplished by means of a stripper foil intersecting the circulating beam. The newly formed positive ions leave the machine through a trajectory whose curvature is opposite to that of the orbit. An upper energy limit to this method may result from beam loss by electric dissociation of the ions. In fact, moving ions in a magnetic field are subjected to an equivalent electric field $E = v \times B$, which at high energies may be strong enough to break them up. Existing projects, however, assume that this loss will not be important at H^- energies as high as 600 MeV.

Other meson factories are based on what is known as a ring cyclotron or separated orbit cyclotron. In spite of its name, this machine bears little resemblance with classical cyclotrons. Particles are injected at rather high energy from another accelerator (for example an AVF cyclotron) and therefore the central part is missing. The low field or valley regions are simply zero field regions, whereas the field in the hills is produced by independent magnets. The machine thus has a synchrotron-like structure, as shown in Fig. 7.20. It illustrates a 510-MeV project for the Swiss Federal Institute of Technology as presented at the 1966 Conference on Isochronous Cyclotrons (Blaser and Willax, 1966).

The *average* magnetic field in these machines is shaped to fulfil the conditions for isochronism (implying constant radio-frequency) at all radii. But the field in the individual magnets can be chosen to provide any type of focussing required, be it weak, strong (alternating gradient) or edge ($n = 0$, as in the ZGS) focussing. This of course introduces a desirable degree of flexibility in design.

Acceleration in separated orbit cyclotrons is provided by resonating radio-frequency cavities, as in linear accelerators, operating at frequencies of about 50 Mc/s, which are higher than the orbital frequency by a factor

ISOCHRONOUS ACCELERATOR FOR 500 MeV PROTONS

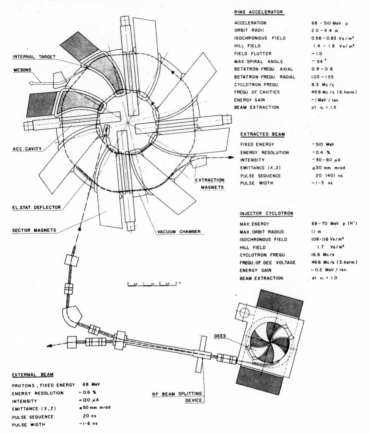

RING ACCELERATOR

ACCELERATION	68 – 510 MeV p
ORBIT RADII	2.0 – 4.4 m
ISOCHRONOUS FIELD	0.58 – 0.83 Vs/m²
HILL FIELD	1.4 – 1.8 Vs/m²
FIELD FLUTTER	~ 1.0
MAX. SPIRAL ANGLE	~ 34°
BETATRON FREQU. AXIAL	0.9 – 0.8
BETATRON FREQU. RADIAL	1.05 – 1.55
CYCLOTRON FREQU.	8.3 Mc/s
FREQU. OF CAVITIES	49.8 Mc/s (6. harm.)
ENERGY GAIN	~1 MeV / rev.
BEAM EXTRACTION	at v_r = 1.5

EXTRACTED BEAM

FIXED ENERGY	~ 510 MeV
ENERGY RESOLUTION	~ 0.4 %
INTENSITY	~ 30 – 80 μA
EMITTANCE (X, Z)	≤ 30 mm mrad
PULSE SEQUENCE	20 (40) ns
PULSE WIDTH	~ 1 – 5 ns

INJECTOR CYCLOTRON

MAX. ENERGY	68 – 70 MeV p (H⁻)
MAX. ORBIT RADIUS	1.1 m
ISOCHRONOUS FIELD	1.08 – 1.16 Vs/m²
HILL FIELD	1.7 Vs/m²
CYCLOTRON FREQU.	16.6 Mc/s
FREQU. OF DEE VOLTAGE	49.8 Mc/s (3. harm.)
ENERGY GAIN	~ 0.2 MeV / rev.
BEAM EXTRACTION	at v_r = 1.0

INTERNAL TARGET

MESONS

ACC. CAVITY

EL. STAT. DEFLECTOR

SECTOR MAGNETS

EXTRACTION MAGNETS

VACUUM CHAMBER

DEES

EXTERNAL BEAM

PROTONS , FIXED ENERGY	68 MeV
ENERGY RESOLUTION	~ 0.6 %
INTENSITY	< 120 μA
EMITTANCE (X, Z)	≤ 50 mm mrad
PULSE SEQUENCE	20 ns
PULSE WIDTH	~ 1 – 6 ns

RF BEAM SPLITTING DEVICE

Fig. 7.20. A project for intense beams of 510 MeV protons. (After Blaser and Willax, 1966).

which may be as large as 20. This factor, called harmonic number, may be changed to adjust the machine for acceleration of heavy ions with various q/m ratios. The energy gain per turn can be very high (a few MeV), providing sufficient separation between orbits to allow almost 100 per cent beam extraction.

In ordinary AVF cyclotrons there is no phase focussing, in the sense that particles can drift out of phase with the fixed radio frequency if the guide field does not fulfil the isochronous condition exactly. This weakness can be avoided in the separated orbit cyclotron by proper use of the design parameters available.

In short, the separated orbit cyclotron can be said to combine the advantages of the isochronous cyclotrons (high-duty cycle, fixed radio frequency, high intensity), the linear accelerator (highly efficient beam extraction) and the synchrocyclotron (phase focussing) in a single accelerator. The most ambitious projects of this kind are those of Chalk River and Oak Ridge. They are three-stage installations, each stage being an accelerator that feeds the next. The intensity of the 1-GeV final proton beam will be 75 mA. This implies enough power in the beam (75 MW) to meet the requirements of a large town.

CHAPTER 8

The Future of Particle Acceleration

1. The Immediate Past

If one wants to investigate the future of a process, the best thing to do is to look into the trends shown in its immediate past. In the case of accelerators the whole history is quite a recent one. It begins in the early thirties with the pioneering work of Cockcroft, Walton, Van de Graaff and Lawrence. It is not a steady drift, but is marked by revolutionary discoveries projecting themselves on all subsequent events. The first is the invention of the cyclotron which, integrated into the more general concept of repeated acceleration in a magnetic guiding field, is present in all circular machines. In 1944 a new idea, that of phase stability, also acquired complete general validity. And lately the principle of strong focussing by alternating gradients has become an important feature of many accelerators.

These few basic principles have been the origin of a large variety of machines. Each type shows a characteristic peculiarity. Let us summarize their features in Table 8.1.

The fixed electric field and single-stage acceleration of the earliest machines was followed by repeated accelerations by means of an alternating electric field in linear accelerators. Repeated acceleration plus a magnetic guiding field led to circular accelerators. Of these, the cyclotron has a fixed field and radio frequency, whilst the betatron is based on the variation of the magnetic field in time. The combination of fixed field and modulated frequency defines the synchrocyclotron and the inverse combination, namely variable field and constant radio frequency, is characteristic of the electron synchrotron. There is only one arrangement left, that of variable radio frequency and field, leading to the proton synchrotron. This is a line of evolution in which higher and higher energies have been attained through successive changes in the time dependence of electric and magnetic fields. This conceptually simple resource has brought about increasing technological complexities. The first applications of strong focussing forces did not reverse this trend, but the azi-

TABLE 8.1
Main Features of Particle Accelerators

Name	Particle	Time variation of electric field	R.F.	Magnetic field depends on	Orbit radius	Energy range
Cockcroft–Walton	e, p, d, α	Constant	—	—	∞	0–1·5 MeV
Van de Graaff	e, p, d, α	Constant	—	—	∞	0–20 MeV
Proton linear	p	R.F.	Constant	—	∞	10–200 MeV
Electron linear	e	R.F.	Constant	—	∞	10–45 000 MeV
Cyclotron	p, d, α	R.F.	Constant	r	Variable	2–20 MeV
Betatron	e	—	—	r, t	Constant	1–200 MeV
Synchrocyclotron	p, d, α	R.F.	Variable	r	Variable	30–780 MeV
Electron synchrotron	e	R.F.	Constant	r, t	Constant	1–600 MeV
Proton synchrotron	p	R.F.	Variable	r, t	Constant	1–10 GeV
A.G. electron synchrotron	e	R.F.	Constant	r, θ, t	Constant	1–7 GeV
A.G. proton synchrotron	p	R.F.	Variable	r, θ, t	Constant	7–200 GeV
A.V.F. cyclotron	p, d, α	R.F.	Constant	r, θ	Variable	10–800 MeV
F.F.A.G. betatron	e	—	—	r, θ (variable flux)	Variable	20–200 MeV
F.F.A.G. synchrotrons	e, p	R.F.	Variable	r, θ	Variable	?

r, radius; θ, azimuthal angle; t, time

muthally varying field cyclotrons and the proposals of fixed field alternating gradient synchrotrons, to be described below, mark a turning point. Variation in time is replaced by variation in space. The aim is not only higher energies but also greater simplicity and economy and a reinforcement of the beam intensity. This will certainly be the characteristic tendency of future investigations on accelerators. Moreover, a trend towards higher intensities is the necessary consequence of past developments in the field of accelerator research.

Let us look at the way in which the energy has increased with time. Every type of machine has had its own evolution, starting with small experimental models and soon reaching the energy limits set by economical or technical considerations. This is what can be seen from Fig. 8.1, where the energies reached by different accelerators are plotted on a logarithmic scale as a function of time. The envelope of the individual evolutions is very close to a straight line. That is to say, the energy depends exponentially on time, increasing by a factor of ten about every five years. At the same time, the beam intensities provided by the highest energy accelerators also follow an exponential law, but *decreasing* with time. This at least was the tendency until 1960. If both curves are extrapolated towards the future, the prediction is that in 1990 we shall be able to accelerate *two protons per hour up to 10 million GeV*! Several generations would have to work with this machine to perform a single experiment. It is now understandable how important are the present efforts to obtain higher intensities. The latest proton synchrotrons, in fact, introduced a dramatic change in the slope of the intensity line, and even higher beam intensities are expected in future machines.

2. The Immediate Future

The design and construction of a high-energy accelerator is a slow enough process to allow an easy forecast of the most important events expected in the field in a few years to come. It is clear that the possibilities of the alternating gradient principle are far from being exhausted, and the first steps will be directed towards its application in a more or less conventional fashion.

Another strong focussing proton synchrotron, with an energy of 70 GeV, became operational at Serpukhov, U.S.S.R., in September 1967. This machine more than duplicates the maximum energy available elsewhere (33 GeV in the Brookhaven synchrotron). In the U.S.A., on the

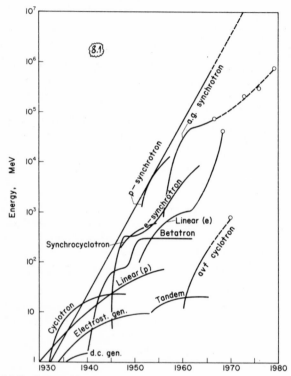

Fig. 8.1. Evolution of the energies attained with accelerators and its extrapolation toward the future, in view of existing projects.

other hand, a detailed study has been conducted at the Lawrence Radiation Laboratory for a 200-GeV giant accelerator. If funds are authorized by Congress in 1967 the machine could be ready by 1973. A few years later a 300-GeV facility may become available at CERN, followed perhaps in the late seventies in the U.S.A. by an 800-GeV accelerator, 3 miles in diameter.

It is worth describing in some detail the 200-GeV project. No new principles are incorporated, but the design is rather unconventional (Fig. 8.2). The machine will be a system of four accelerators, feeding one

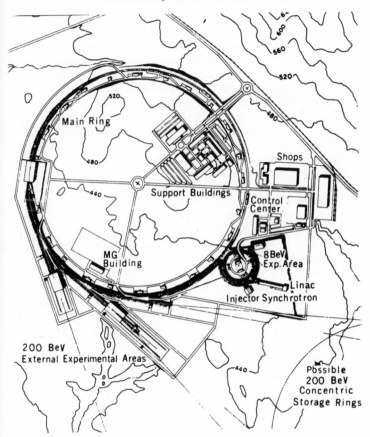

Fig. 8.2. System of accelerators and ancillary buildings in the 200-GeV project.
(*By courtesy of the Lawrence Radiation Laboratory*).

another in series. The first, a Cockcroft-Walton generator, will inject 750 keV protons into a 200-MeV, 160-m long linear accelerator. This arrangement will serve as a pre-injector into an 8-GeV injector synchrotron, 216 m in diameter, which in turn will deliver high-energy protons into the main accelerator. The latter will be a strong focussing machine with 500 magnets in the ring, about 1 500 m in diameter.

This 'series' design is very efficient from the point of view of the acceptance of alternating gradient accelerators. If the vacuum chamber is filled at injection with particles of all possible coordinates and momenta, it will become rather 'empty' at high energies, although containing the same number of particles, because of the progressive damping of oscillations of all types. It can be said that the acceptance increases as the particles gain energy. Acceleration in a single ring results in some waste of phase space*, but this waste is relatively less important as the injection energy increases. Hence the use of a single ring to accelerate from very low to very high energies is inconvenient from the point of view of beam intensity. For this reason two rings, and high injection energy in both, have been chosen in the 200-GeV project. One should note the large radius of the injector synchrotron, compared, for example, with the 23·6 m of the 7-GeV NIMROD (cf. Table 6.2). It is a low-field, large-aperture machine, admitting operation at a high repetition rate. Seven proton bursts from this machine will fill the vacuum chamber of the main synchrotron, which will deliver 3×10^{13} protons per pulse, thirty times a minute. This corresponds to an average current of 2·5 μA, about thirty times greater than that available from present proton synchrotrons. It is expected that this intensity will allow the performance of 10 to 15 simultaneous experiments, as well as the production of beams of secondary particles (hyperons, for example) not available at present.

If the cost estimates given for this machine are accurate, it will result in an economical record. The expected total cost is 280 million dollars, that is, 0·0014 dollars/eV, the cheapest unit cost in the history of accelerators (wholesale price, of course).

3. Fixed Field Alternating Gradient Synchrotrons

The low value of the momentum compaction factor is an essential feature of strong focussing acceleration. Particles of widely different energies move in relatively close orbits. This fact has induced scientists of the

---

* The phase space is a 6-dimensional space for each particle, whose coordinate axes are the components of the momentum and position vectors of the particle. The acceptance of an accelerator is simply the volume in phase space comprising the coordinates and momenta of all particles that will not be lost in the course of subsequent acceleration.

MURA (Midwestern Universities Research Association) group in the United States to abandon the idea of acceleration at a fixed radius with a variable magnetic guiding field. Instead, a fixed field alternating gradient (commonly abbreviated FFAG magnet) would accommodate all orbits of different radii, from injection up to final energy, in a ring-shaped acceleration chamber (Symon, 1955; Symon *et al.*, 1956). The same principle was conceived independently by L. J. Haworth at Brookhaven, T. Okhawa in Japan and A. A. Kolomenskii in the U.S.S.R. No FFAG proton synchrotron has yet been built, but the soundness of the theoretical principles involved has been tested in small experimental models accelerating electrons (Jones *et al.*, 1959; MURA Staff, 1964).

A fixed magnetic field simplifies enormously the construction of a machine. Moreover, in this case the acceleration cycle depends only on the frequency variation. As this may be much faster than a change in the magnetic field, there can be more beam bursts per second and consequently a higher beam intensity than in the usual case.

The magnetic field must fulfil a supplementary condition: the number of betatron oscillations on any of the orbits must not be an integer. Furthermore, the choice of the operating point inside one of the stable diamonds of Fig. 7.8 implies that this number must be the same for all orbits, irrespective of energy. Otherwise the operating point may cross a resonance as the orbit is changing continuously. Since the radial and vertical betatron oscillations depend mainly on the field index k, a possible field satisfying this requirement is, in the median plane,

$$B = B_0(r/r_0)^k f(N\theta) , \qquad (8.1)$$

where

$$k = \frac{r}{B} \frac{\partial B}{\partial r} = \text{const.}$$

$f(N\theta)$ is a function of period 2π, accounting for the alternating structure of the field with angle θ, and N is the number of periods in the guide field.

Two field configurations, corresponding to different choices of $f(N\theta)$ in eqn. (8.1), have been studied by the MURA group. They are known as 'radial sector' and 'spiral ridge' fields.

The periods in a radial sector synchrotron consist of two magnets producing fields of opposite sign. The resulting orbits show the scalloped shape of Fig. 8.3. The machine is therefore about five times longer than it would

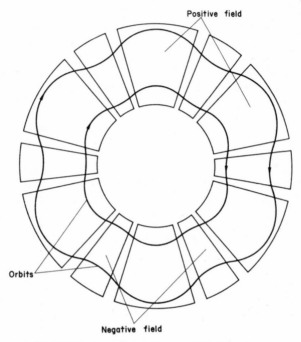

Fig. 8.3. Structure of a radial sector FFAG machine.

be if the negative field sectors were absent, but the expected increase in beam intensity amply compensates for the additional cost involved. An interesting property of this configuration is that the momentum compaction factor can be made either positive or negative, which implies that the final orbit can be the largest or the smallest, at will.

The pole tips required to produce the spiral ridge field look like furrowed surfaces in which there is a succession of peaks and valleys (Fig. 8.4). Peaks in both pole faces oppose each other, and the field between them is correspondingly reinforced. A spiral ridge machine need not be much longer than other strong focussing synchrotrons.

The magnets producing the required field distributions in both configurations are extremely complicated. A side view of the magnet

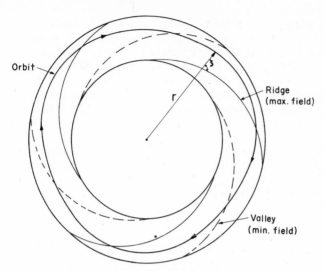

Fig. 8.4. Spiral ridge FFAG accelerator.

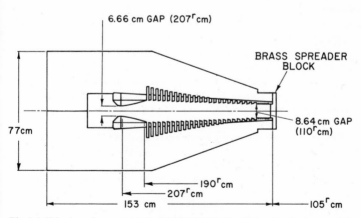

Fig. 8.5. Side view of a magnet in the MURA 50-MeV radial sector electron model.
(After Haxby *et al.*, 1964. Copyright USAEC).

structure used in the MURA 50-MeV radial sector electron model is shown in Fig. 8.5 (Haxby, 1964). Auxiliary windings are placed in the slots cut in the poles, adjusting the field variation with radius to that prescribed in eqn. (8.1) with $k \simeq 9.3$. The maximum field in this machine is 5 kG, well below the saturation limits of the iron yoke.

A useful figure for comparison of the merits of different synchrotrons is the relative radial aperture. Its average value is 0.51 in the 50-MeV model, although it is expected that with proper advance in magnet design it may be as small as 0.02 in a full-size machine. This value is of the same order of magnitude as that of a weak-focussing synchrotron, and about ten times greater than that of an ordinary alternating gradient machine.

The proposal of FFAG accelerators paved the way for even bolder suggestions. One of them is that of beam stacking, which we shall describe below.

We have already mentioned that the acceleration capability of a strong focussing synchrotron increases with the beam energy. That is to say, if the machine can accept a certain number of particles at injection, it could handle many more once they have reached, say, half the final energy. A FFAG synchrotron can take full advantage of this fact by beam stacking. In this process a group of particles is accelerated to some desired energy and then is left to circulate while later groups are injected and accelerated. Since the revolution frequency is a function of the particle energy, the accelerating system must be synchronous with the particles that are accelerated and non-synchronous with those in the stacked beam, thereby having little effect on the latter. When the stacked beam has reached full intensity a second radio-frequency system drives it to maximum energy. In practice both systems would operate simultaneously, the second having a lower repetition rate than the first. Alternatively, the beam can be stacked at the final energy, in order to bring it onto a target either in short intense bursts or as a continuous stream of particles, at will.

The mechanism of beam stacking is best described in terms of the motion of 'buckets' in what is called synchrotron phase space (Symon and Sessler, 1956). The coordinates of this space are φ, the relative phase of the particle with respect to the accelerating voltage, and S, defined by

$$S = \int_{W_0}^{W} \frac{\mathrm{d}W}{f(W)}, \tag{8.2}$$

where $f(W)$ is the frequency of revolution of the particle as a function of its total energy W. The coordinates φ and S have the interesting property of being canonical variables, like the momentum components and coordinates of a particle. That is, their time derivatives can be obtained from a single function H (the Hamiltonian) by means of the canonical equations

$$\dot{\varphi} = \frac{\partial H}{\partial S}, \qquad (8.3)$$

$$\dot{S} = -\frac{\partial H}{\partial \varphi}, \qquad (8.4)$$

where

$$H = (\omega - \omega_s)S + qV\cos\varphi \qquad (8.5)$$

if radiation losses are not taken into account. In fact, according to eqn. (6.2), $\dot{\varphi} = \omega - \omega_s$, and

$$\dot{S} = \frac{dS}{dW}\frac{dW}{dt} = qV\sin\varphi .$$

As a particle performs phase oscillations, its coordinates φ and S describe a line in phase space. This will be a closed curve if the oscillations are stable, an open one otherwise. The region of phase space containing all possible closed curves described by the equations of motion is called a 'bucket'. Such regions are shown in Figs. 8.6 and 8.7, corresponding to Hamiltonians where $\omega_s = $ const. (stationary bucket, $\varphi_s = 0$) and the radio frequency is a function of the time (moving bucket, $\varphi_s \neq 0$), respectively. In the first case the synchronous energy is constant, in the second the synchronous energy can increase or decrease, depending on the modulation of the radio frequency.

The advantage of the canonical formalism is that certain general theorems of statistical mechanics can be applied. One of them is Liouville's theorem, which states that the transformation of a closed curved in phase space under the equations of motion is such that the enclosed area remains constant. The density of particles inside a bucket is therefore also constant when acted upon by an ideal radio-frequency system.

The stacking process in the MURA 50-MeV electron accelerator (Symon *et al.*, 1964) is based on these ideas. The particles are betatron accelerated by means of four magnetic cores inside the machine. A fixed-frequency accelerating system is then switched on, the voltage increasing slowly until the particles have been captured into a stationary bucket of

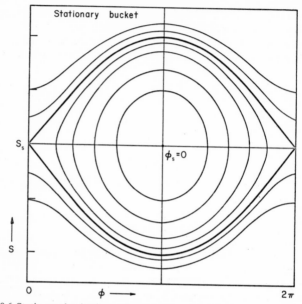

Fig. 8.6. Stationary bucket in synchrotron phase space. (After Symon *et al.*, 1964).

sufficient size. The voltage is subsequently kept constant, while the radio frequency decreases following the frequency of revolution of a particle of increasing energy. The particles are therefore accelerated inside a moving bucket, until they reach the stacking energy.

The problem of stacking the beam for about one second or more has been solved by the MURA group using what is known as 'phase displacement' acceleration (Jones *et al.*, 1959). In principle, one has to make up for the radiation loss of the revolving beam, which at 50 MeV is about 3 eV per turn. If the beam is to be stacked in a stationary bucket by an auxiliary radio-frequency system, the bucket must hold the full energy spread of the beam, which may be several MeV, and the accelerating voltage must increase accordingly. Calculations at MURA showed that the required energy gain per turn was 50 keV. Instead, one can choose to decelerate an *empty* bucket from an energy higher than the maximum energy in the beam (where no particles exist) to an energy lower than the

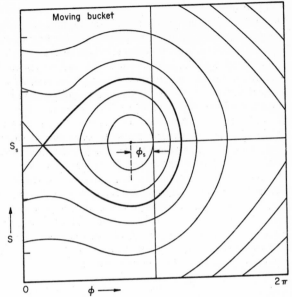

Fig. 8.7. Moving bucket in synchrotron phase space. (After Symon *et al.*, 1964).

minimum in the beam. The phase space previously occupied by the beam now contains an empty bucket, while the stacked beam, according to Liouville's theorem, has been displaced *upwards* in energy. In this way an accelerating voltage of only 500 V was found to be sufficient. The phase displacement system is turned on during the intervals between the arrival of different beam pulses at the stacking energy. The radio frequency starts being synchronous with the particles of highest energy and is modulated to synchronism with the lowest energy, when it is suddenly turned off. Several sweeps of this type can be made through the same beam. The 50-MeV machine has reached stacked beam intensities of 5·6 A using this process.

We do not know if a full-size FFAG proton accelerator will ever be built. But there is no doubt that the underlaying ideas will strongly influence the future of particle acceleration.

4. Colliding Brams

Taking for granted that future accelerators will deliver very intense beams of energetic particles, we may ask how far up in energy those machines will go. A discouraging fact appears when very high energies are sought. Whatever the interaction between two particles, the motion of their centre of mass will remain unperturbed. In actual experiments, a fast particle collides with another at rest in the target, which is in turn fixed in the laboratory. But the physics of the situation is best described in the centre-of-mass $(C\text{-})$ system of coordinates, where the centre of mass is assumed to be at rest and the particles encounter each other moving with opposite velocities. If both particles are identical (protons, for example), their velocities are the same in this system. In the laboratory $(L\text{-})$ system, on the other hand, a fraction of the available kinetic energy is associated with the motion of the centre of mass, and is therefore lost for the inter-action. This fraction becomes more important as the energy increases. In fact, according to the theory of relativity, the quantity $W^2 - p^2 c^2$ for a number of particles has the same value in all systems of coordinates (it is equal to the rest energy squared in the particular case of a single particle). Since the total momentum in the C-system is zero,

$$W_C^2 = W_L^2 - p_L^2 c^2 \,, \tag{8.6}$$

where the subscripts refer to the C- and L-systems. In the case of two identical particles, the momentum of the moving particle in the L-system can be expressed as

$$p_L = mv = \frac{W_L - W_o}{c}\,\beta = \frac{W_L - W_o}{c}\sqrt{\left[1 - \left(\frac{W_o}{W_L - W_o}\right)^2\right]} \tag{8.7}$$

where W_o denotes the rest energy of *one* particle. Replacing (8.7) in (8.6) one obtains

$$W_C/W_o = (2W_L/W_o)^{\frac{1}{2}} \,, \tag{8.8}$$

which shows that the total energy in the C-system increases only as the square root of the L-energy.

Many of the experiments in high-energy physics study proton-proton collisions. A tremendous increase in the available energy would be obtained if the L-system were physically transformed in the C-system by making two proton beams collide against one another. According to eqn. (8.8), the kinetic energy in a collision between two 15-GeV protons corresponds to the conventional arrangement where the moving proton has 540 GeV. The question is: how does one manage to put two high-energy protons together in space and time? It must be kept in mind that the highest particle density ever obtained in an accelerated proton beam is smaller by a few orders of magnitude than that of the residual gas in the chamber. Since the number of interactions per second is proportional to the product of particle densities, collisions with the molecules of residual gas produce a large background of unwanted events which may eventually mask the true interactions taking place in the colliding beams. The only answer to this problem is very intense beams and very high vacua. In spite of the difficulties outlined, the high intensities expected from FFAG accelerators have stimulated the serious consideration of such experiments. Moreover, if the positive and negative sectors in a radial sector FFAG synchrotron are made of the same length and have the same magnetic field intensity, particles can be accelerated simultaneously in both directions. A single two-way accelerator (Petukhov, 1957; Okhawa, 1958) can therefore provide intense colliding beams. MURA's 50-MeV machine has indeed been used for the acceleration of two counter-revolving electron beams up to 27 MeV, where they were destroyed by resonant effects arising from field imperfections.

The MURA group has studied the feasibility of a two-way 15-GeV proton synchrotron. Both beams should have intensities of about 800 A (the present figure is about 10^{-7} A) to provide an acceptable number of interactions per second. Such intensities could be achieved by the stacking of 10 000 buckets by the method described above. The pressure in the acceleration chamber should be about 10^{-9} mm Hg (a thousand times lower than the usual ones at present) to reduce the background of inter-actions with molecules of residual gas to about 10 per cent of those due to the intersecting beams.

As an alternative to two-way accelerators, the functions of acceleration and storage can be split into different structures. In such arrangements a single accelerator would alternatingly feed two storage magnetic rings, as shown in Fig. 8.8. The advantage is that a fixed-field magnetic ring, where the beam is simply stored and no further acceleration takes place, is much easier to build than a complete accelerator. Furthermore, such storage rings can be added to existing accelerators. Two projects of this type will probably take form in a few years: a storage ring pair for the CERN synchrotron, providing reaction energies equivalent to a 2 200-GeV

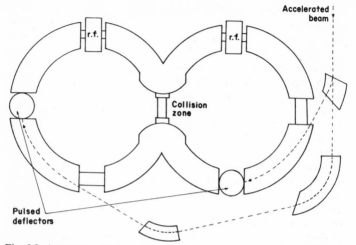

Fig. 8.8. Arrangement of two storage rings for colliding-beam experiments.

conventional arrangement, and an electron-positron ring for the electron accelerator now under construction at Stanford. In the latter facility two beams of about 3-GeV electrons and positrons will travel in opposite directions within a single ring, producing interactions corresponding to an *L*-energy of 60 000 GeV. In this way it is expected to check quantum electrodynamics down to distances of about 10^{-15} cm. In both proton and electron storage rings simple radio-frequency systems must be installed, serving the purpose of keeping the particles within a stationary bucket and compensating radiation losses.

5. New Principles

The novelty of the preceding proposals does not go far enough to sever an ultimate link with the past: the electric fields providing acceleration are still generated on metallic electrodes, the magnetic guiding fields require conventional magnets with iron yokes. The maximum field attainable is then, because of the saturation conditions of iron, 20 000 gauss. With this limit the radius of the accelerator yielding 10 million GeV protons by 1 990 would be 10 000 miles. The Equator would be too short to accommodate this machine!

A way out of the restrictions set by the iron is, of course, the use of ironless coils to generate the magnetic field. Based on this idea, the construction of a 10-GeV proton synchrotron has been started in Australia. A peak field of 80 000 gauss is expected, allowing the rather small diameter of 10 m. But the generator supplying the 1·6 million amperes needed in the coils limits the repetition rate to one beam burst every ten minutes. An interesting fact is that the mechanical forces acting on adjacent windings reach 16 tons/cm.

It is possible that further development of superconducting magnets may find an application in the accelerator field. In these magnets the coils are made of superconductive material, which loses all electrical resistance when cooled down to very low temperatures. In this way stable fields of about 50 000 gauss have been obtained in rather restricted volumes. Their use in accelerators would demand an increase of many orders of magnitude not only in the size of the existing magnets, but also of the cryogenic stations producing the liquid helium used as a coolant in these studies.

A fundamental break-through in the very principles of particle acceleration and focussing may be the next step. It is necessary, if progress is to continue at the same pace. Many new ideas were advanced a few years ago at the 1956 CERN Symposium on High Energy Accelerators and Pion Physics, and still require further study. We shall mention briefly some of them, referring the reader to the Proceedings of the Symposium for a more extensive treatment.

Several suggestions pointed to the importance that plasmas (fully ionized gases) may have in future developments. It has been shown, for instance, that a waveguide filled with a completely ionized gas would furnish the framework in which a linear accelerator could provide radial and phase stability simultaneously.

An alternative to the usual guiding magnetic field has been proposed by Budker. As is well known, a current flowing in a conductor creates a magnetic field not only outside the conductor, but also inside. If the conductor has a cylindrical cross-section of radius r_0, the field becomes, in mks units

$$B = 10^{-7} \, 2Ir/r_0^2 \,,$$

where I is the total current and $r < r_0$. The same formula applies to a stream of electrons of cylindrical cross-section. If one were able to create a beam carrying 10 000 A in the form of a filament of only 0·02 mm radius, the field would change from zero on the axis of the beam to one million gauss on the surface. Furthermore, if the electron beam follows a closed orbit it could provide the guide field for the acceleration of protons, with very strong focussing forces in *all* directions corresponding to n values of about 10^6. The protons would move on the axis of the electron beam at zero energy and 0.02 mm away at final energy. With the above figures a 100-GeV proton accelerator would have a radius of 3 m.

Pending questions are how such an intense electron beam can be generated and whether, once formed, it will be stable for a sufficiently long time to allow the acceleration of the protons. There exists a reasonable hope for a positive answer to the second question. In fact, in addition to the repulsion forces between individual electrons due to their electric charge, attractive magnetic forces appear as a result of their motion. Each moving electron is equivalent to a current filament, and the individual currents attract each other. In the relativistic limit the magnetic force just compensates the charge repulsion. The addition of a few positive ions to the electron beam should result in a further neutralization of the charge and make the beam shrink to a very small diameter under the action of the magnetic force. This is similar to the 'pinch effect' of plasma physics, although in the latter case the problem of inherent instabilities has not yet been solved. In Budker's project the betatron oscillations induced by collisions with the ions would be heavily damped because of the radiation losses, which in turn would be compensated by betatron acceleration of the electron beam. However, many sources of instabilities may still remain, such as those due to the accelerated proton beam reacting on the electron beam.

The generation of such intensities of relativistic electrons is still an open question. Preliminary results have been reported on a 10-A current of electrons accelerated to 3 MeV.

Still more far-reaching is the 'principle of coherent acceleration', put forward by Veksler. According to this principle there are certain physical processes which may eventually lead to the acceleration of particles, and are actually reinforced according to the number of participating particles. As an example, we may consider a bunch of relativistic electrons with a total mass M_1 colliding with a bunch of protons at rest, having a total mass M_2. If the masses are such that $M_1 \gg M_2\gamma$, where $\gamma^2 = 1/(1-\beta^2)$, it can be shown with the use of relativistic mechanics that the stationary group will be left, after a head-on collision, with the total energy $M_2 c^2 \gamma^2$.

Taking $\gamma = 10^2$, corresponding to 50-MeV electrons, one finds that each proton will acquire a total energy equal to 10 000 times its rest energy, that is, 9 380 GeV. The validity of this result depends on both bunches acting collectively and not through the individual particles. It is not clear how this can be achieved.

The possibilities of electron clouds providing positive ion acceleration have been examined in a recent paper (Janes *et al.*, 1965). In this proposal an electron cloud is contained along the circular axis of a torus by a magnetic field parallel to the axis (Fig. 8.9). Such a charge distribution produces an electric field directed towards the axis, where a potential minimum exists. The individual electrons drift in the combined electric and magnetic fields satisfying the equilibrium condition $\mathbf{E} + \mathbf{v} \times \mathbf{B} = 0$. This condition simply expresses the balance of electric and magnetic forces on each electron and determines its drift velocity. The electron

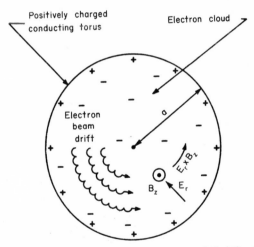

Fig. 8.9. Generation of strong electric fields by electron drift. (After Janes *et al.*, 1965).

cloud can be formed by injecting the electrons as the magnetic field builds up. The increase in magnetic flux density can be regarded as a concentration of magnetic lines of force towards the axis. Low-energy electrons are trapped by the lines of force, which carry them into the system, performing the same function as the belt in a Van de Graaff machine. In this case, however, there is no insulator separating two electrodes. Moreover, the difficulties associated with the emission of electrons from a negative terminal are eliminated. Preliminary estimates indicate that fields in excess of 10^8 V/cm should be feasible. Such fields could be used for the acceleration of positive ions, which would precipitate towards the axis and produce nuclear reactions there. The authors expect a meson production rate of 10^{16} per second with a 1-GeV machine having a torus of only 1 m radius. This machine would require, however, the rather large magnetic field of 100 kilogauss. On a smaller scale, a 10-MeV machine comparable with a Van de Graaff can be reached with a torus of 10 cm radius at magnetic fields of 50 kilogauss.

Bibliography

LIVINGSTON, M.S. and BLEWETT, J.P. (1962) *Particle Accelerators*, McGraw-Hill Book Co., New York. An advanced textbook, containing detailed information on general principles and their application to individual machines. *Encyclopedia of Physics (Handbuch der Physik)*, (1959), **XLIV** Springer, Berlin. Thorough descriptions of different types of accelerators by specialists in the field.

References

ADAMS, J.B., HINE, M.G.N. and LAWSON, J.D. (1953) *Nature* **171**, 926.

BENNETT, W.H. and DARBY, P.F. (1936) *Phys. Rev.* **49**, 97, 422, 881.

BLASER, J.P. and WILLAX, H.A. (1966) International Conference on Isochronous Cyclotrons, Gatlinburg, Tennessee. *IEE Transactions on Nuclear Science*, NS. **13**, 451.

BOHM, D. and FOLDY, L.L. (1946) *Phys. Rev.* **70**, 249.

BOHM, D. and FOLDY, L.L. (1947) *Phys. Rev.* **72**, 649.

COCKCROFT, J.D. and WALTON, E.T.S. (1932) *Proc. Roy. Soc. (London)* **A 136**, 619, **A 137**, 229.

COSMOTRON STAFF. (1953) *Rev. Sci. Instr.* **24**, 723.

COURANT, E.D. LIVINGSTON, M.S. and SNYDER, H.S. (1952) *Phys. Rev.* **88**, 1190.

DICKSON, J.M. (1961) *International Conference as High Energy Accelerators*, p. 119.

HENDERSON, C., HEYMANN, F.F. and JENNINGS, R.E. 1953. *Proc. Phys. Soc. (London)* **66 B**, 41.

JANES, G.S., LEVY, R.H. and PETSHEK, H.E. (1965) *Phys. Rev. Lett.* **15**, 138.

JONES, L.W., PRUETT, C.H., SYMON, K.R. and TERWILLIGER, K.M. (1959) *Proceedings of the Internat. Conf. on High Energy Acc. and Instrum.*, CERN, Geneva, p. 58.

180 *References*

KERST, D.W. and SERBER, R. (1941) *Phys. Rev.* **60**, 53.

KERST, D.W. (1948) *Phys. Rev.* **74**, 503.

DE KRUIFF, G.T. and VERSTER, N.F. (1961/1962) *Philips Technical Review* **23**, 381.

LAWRENCE, E.O. and EDLEFSEN, N.E. (1930) *Science* **72**, 376.

LAWRENCE, E.O. and LIVINGSTON, M.S. (1931) *Phys. Rev.* **37**, 1707, **38**, 136.

LAWRENCE, E.O. and LIVINGSTON, M.S. (1932) *Phys. Rev.* **40**, 19.

LE COUTEUR, K.J. and LIPTON, S. (1956) *Phil. Mag.* **46**, 1265.

Linear Accelerator Issue (1955) *Rev. Sci. Instr.* **26**, II.

LORRAIN, P., BEIQUE, R., GILMORE, P., GIRARD, P.E., BRETON, A. and PICHÉ, P. (1957) *Can. J. Phys.* **35**, 299.

MCMILLAN, E.M.C. (1945) *Phys. Rev.* **68**, 143.

MURA STAFF (1964) *Rev. Sci. Instr.* **35**, 1393.

OKHAWA, T. (1958)*Rev. Sci. Instr.* **29**, 108.

OLIPHANT, M.L., GOODEN, J.S. and HIDE, G.S. (1947) *Proc. Phys. Soc. (London)*, **59**, 666.

PARKINSON, D.H. (1962) *British J. Appl. Phys.* **13**, 49.

PETUKHOV, V.A. (1957) *Zh. Eksperim. i Teor. Fiz.* **32**, 379. (Engl. tr. 1957. *Soviet Physics JETP* **5**, 317.)

SYMON, K.R. (1955) *Phys. Rev.* **98**, 1152A.

SYMON, K.R., KERST, D.W., JONES, L.W., LASLETT, L.J. and TERWILLIGER, K.M. (1956) *Phys. Rev.* **103**, 1837.

SYMON, K.R. and SESSLER, A.M. (1956) *Proc. CERN Symp. on High Energy Accelerators and Pion Physics*, Geneva, **I**, 44.

SYMON, K.R., ROWE, E.M., SWENSON, D.A. and JOHNSTON, L.H. (1964) *Rev. Sci. Instr.* **35**, 1459.

THOMAS, L.H. (1938) *Phys. Rev.* **54**, 580.

TUCK, J.L. and TENG, L.C. (1951) *Phys. Rev.* **81**, 1305.

VAN DE GRAAFF, R.J. (1931) *Phys. Rev.* **38**, 1919A.

VAN DE GRAAFF, R.J. (1960) *Nuclear Instruments & Methods* **8**, 195.

VAN DE GRAAFF, R.J., ROSE, P.H. and WITTKOWER, A.B. (1962) *Nature* **195**, 1292.

VEKSLER, V. (1944) *Compt. Rend. Acad. Sci. U.S.S.R.* **43**, 444; **44**, 393.

VEKSLER, V. (1945) *J. Phys. (U.S.S.R.)* **9**, 153.

VLADIMIRSKII, V.V. and TARASOV, E.K. (1956) *Zh. Techn. Fiz. (U.S.S.R.)* **26**, 704.

WIDERÖE, R. (1928) *Arch. Elektrotech.* **21**, 387.

Index